THE
TOTAL
WOMAN

A Holistic Approach to Life Balance

Wellness. Relationships. Self-Confidence. Business.

Edited by

Linda Ellis Eastman

Professional Woman Publishing
Prospect, Kentucky

The Total Woman
Copyright © 2019 by Linda Ellis Eastman

Published by:
Professional Woman Publishing
Post Office Box 333
Prospect, KY 40059
(502) 228-0906
www.pwnbooks.com

Please contact the publisher for quantity discounts.

ISBN 13: 978-1-7325088-2-8

Library of Congress Cataloging-In-Publication Data

Printed in the United States of America

TABLE OF CONTENTS

TABLE OF CONTENTS

TABLE OF CONTENTS

ABOUT THE AUTHOR

LINDA ELLIS EASTMAN

Linda Ellis Eastman is President and CEO of The Professional Woman Network (PWN), an International Training and Consulting Organization on Women's Issues. She has designed seminars which have been presented in China, the former Soviet Union, South Africa, the Phillipines, and attended by individuals in the United States from such firms as McDonalds, USA Today, Siemens-Westinghouse, the Pentagon, the Department of Defense, and the United States Department of Education.

An expert on women's issues, Ms. Eastman has certified and trained over four thousand women to start consulting/seminar businesses originating from such countries as Pakistan, the Ukraine, Antigua, Canada, Mexico, Zimbabwe, Nigeria, Bermuda, Jamaica, Costa Rica, England, South Africa, Malaysia, and Kenya. Founded in 1982 by Linda Ellis Eastman, The Professional Woman Network is committed to educating women on a global basis regarding, self-esteem, confidence building, stress management, and emotional, mental, spiritual and physical wellness.

Ms. Eastman has been featured in USA Today and listed in Who's Who of American Women, as well as Who's Who of International Leaders. In addition to women's issues, Ms. Eastman speaks internationally regarding the importance of human respect as it relates to race, color, culture, age, and gender. Annually, she facilitates an international conference where speakers and participants from many nations discuss issues that are unique to women on a global basis.

Linda Ellis Eastman is also founder of The Professional Woman Speakers Bureau and The Professional Woman Coaching Institute. Ms. Eastman has dedicated her businesses to increasing the self-esteem and personal dignity of women and youth around the world.

Contact:
The Professional Woman Network
P.O. Box 333
Prospect, KY 40059
(502) 345-4139
lindaeastman@prodigy.net
www.pwnbooks.com
www.protrain.net

THE
TOTAL
WOMAN

A Holistic Approach to Life Balance
Wellness. Relationships. Self-Confidence. Business.

ABOUT THE AUTHOR

DR MARISSA MAGSINO FAARFM

For 20 years, Dr. Magsino had dedicated her practice to treating various diseases and medical conditions. In 2006, with the onset of premenopausal symptoms, she began her journey to find a natural way to replace her own hormones. She pursued a fellowship in Functional and Regenerative Medicine centered on bio-identical hormone management.

While working through her own physical challenges of stress incontinence, she received innovative stem cell therapy procedures and noticed incredible facial and vaginal rejuvenation. This personal experience inspired her to create BUMATAKO, and through her own practice, she has become one of the few physicians in the U.S. trained to perform PRP procedures on the face, vaginal and penile areas for rejuvenation.

BUMATAKO, a Filipino term meaning "I'm young again," is an iconic representation of Dr. Magsino's personal journey of reverse aging, beginning with hormone balancing and the revolutionary process of PRP to rejuvenate the body.

She received her medical degree from the University of the East (Philippines) and Internal Medicine/ Pediatrics training at University of Medicine and Dentistry in Newark, New Jersey in 1997. Her passion for helping others earned her awards as top 100 global Filipina in 2018 and Health Ambassador of Modern Widow's Club USA.

Contact:
Drmmagsino@gmail.com

ONE

Happy Life Now A Paradigm Shift to Functional Medicine

Marissa Magsino MD, FAARBM

"Youth is not a time of life it is a state of mind, it is not a matter of rosy cheeks, red lips and supple knees, it is a matter of the will, a quality of the imagination a vigor of the emotions, it is the freshness of the deep springs of life." — Samuel Ullman

I live a happy and fulfilled life now after having completely shifted my traditional medical practice to a full Functional Medicine practice. My journey began after 20 years of practicing Internal Medicine in Orlando. I discovered that I was going through mood shifts of anxiety while seeing forty patients a day. I noticed that more stressful reactions followed these mood patterns and led to numerous car accidents. I couldn't work for several months.

I serendipitously discovered menopause and hormones while attending a local convention during that break. I sought a consult with a known Functional Medicine doctor at 42, and discovered self-healing using natural bio-identical hormone replacement therapy.

My own transformational journey inspired me to pursue my passion to seek alternative medical therapies without using numerous pills for every illness. After completing board certification in Functional and Regenerative Medicine in 2009, I began to incorporate these concepts in my traditional practice. Optimizing female hormones equipped me with the strength to weather the storm, the greatest stressor in life after the sudden death of my spouse in 2014. I grieved the loss, but maintained my professional work, keeping my mind focused on the tasks at hand. That has led me to find new purpose in life.

How is a paradigm shift to Functional Medicine the new way to be happy?

In today's world, 3,500 women go through menopause a day a physiologic change called menopause defined as cessation of menses for 12 months. Perimenopause is the 10 years prior to this hormonal fluctuation caused by aging ovaries and decline of the production of essential female hormones beginning with progesterone, testosterone and finally estrogen.

Hormones are the key messengers that trigger the ovaries, thyroid gland and adrenals to assist bodily functions that affect moods, weight, desire, sleep and memory.

Testosterone is vital to women and is secreted monthly by the ovaries and is the libido that gives the desire for intimacy. It is an anabolic hormone that has distinguished ability to melt abdominal fat and mobilize energy production, tone muscles and bone tissues. Women ages 20-40 lose 50% of this hormone,thus starting the menopause phase which causes inability to focus, weight gain, low or no libido and saggy muscles.

Progesterone is a female hormone produced monthly by the ovaries and is the first to decline in perimenopause. It is responsible for mood swings such as anxiety, premenstrual symptoms of irritability and depression. One of its functions is to assist in thyroid hormone optimization. It is alsoa natural diuretic and eases swelling and fluid retention, and most of all, it helps with insomnia by inducing relevance in sound sleep patterns.

Estrogen is the last female hormone to decrease with menopause and is exhibited by classic symptoms of hot flushes, vaginal dryness, wrinkles on the face, dryness of the skin and memory loss.

Estradiol is a good estrogen replacement that nourishes brain neurons and prevents dementia. It is also prevents osteoporosis, a phenomenon of bone loss and fragility of big joints leading to fractures in the elderly.

Cortisol is a stress hormone secreted by adrenal glands in afight or flight" neurological response. When there is hormone imbalance, it is perceived as a stressor, thus a cortisol surge occurs followed by symptoms of sugar or salt cravings, insomnia and weight gain in the mid-section. Cortisol is normally secreted at optimum levels in the morning and declines throughout the afternoon. Long term exposure to stress hormones accounts for 75-90% of primary care visits in the US. It is the reason why women eat poorly and also fail to exercise and may also lead to some sort of substance abuse to deal with stress.

Adrenal dysfunction is common in women who are multi-taskers. Lack of sleep and fatigue are the most common symptoms, when not addressed properly, are crucial to weight loss management, immune dysfunction and impaired thinking and performance.

Thyroid hormone is a substance secreted by the butterfly gland around the throat area which is responsible for body metabolism, energy production, memory, hair production and heart functions, to name a few.

Low thyroid or hypothyroidism is very common in menopausal women. It is seen as symptoms of weight gain, memory loss, depression, cold intolerance, menstrual cycle dysfunction, also cholesterol abnormalities and joint pains. The active thyroid hormone, T3, circulating in the blood can be monitored and is important for controlling weight, burning fat and maintaining energy production.

Growth hormone is secreted by the master gland—the pituitary gland and is essential for balanced and optimized hormone harmony. The classic symptoms that accompany lack of growth hormone include fatigue, poor immune function, thinning skin, premature aging, sexual dysfunction and decreased muscle mass and insomnia.

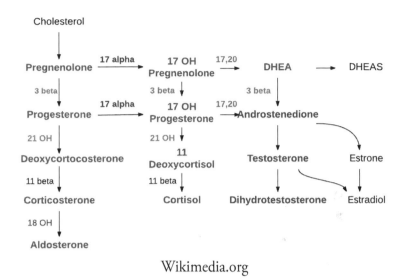

Wikimedia.org

What are the ways to have a happy, healthy life?

It's important to find a doctor who is trained in the field of Functional Medicine or Integrative Medicine. The physiology and biochemistry of the aging process is treated using modalities that are more organic, holistic and avoid the use of "pill for every ill" approach commonly found in modern medicine. A traditional physician would write numerous prescriptions for an aging woman in menopause with several drugs including sleeping pills, anxiolytics for anxiety, antidepressant and appetite suppressants. The value of optimized health is to function and have the energy of a younger woman and to age well.

TIP: To find your local Functional Medicine trained physician visit worldhealth.net.

Follow these steps as a guide on your visit to your Functional Medicine doctor:

1. Know your hormonal age and status and incorporate "body identical" hormones. It means using compounded bioidentical hormones personalized to each patient's hormone levels. It comes in variety of forms, from troches (a small tablet or lozenge), oral capsules, transdermal creams and pellets (rice grain hormones implanted subcutaneously into fatty tissue).

Know the facts—there is a difference in hormone replacement using bio identical or body identical versus conventional or synthetic hormone replacement,

In early 2000, the Women's Health Initiative Trial showed that when using synthetic hormone replacement, there was a 41% increase in strokes, 20% increase in heart attacks and 26% increase in breast cancer and 76% increase in Alzheimer's dementia. Many doctors stopped prescribing the synthetic hormones due to fear of the above only with the advent of bioidentical hormones when they showed the benefits of replacing hormones using organic, natural hormones made from yam or soy.

2. Know your micronutrients. Supplements are vital in optimized hormone levels. Vitamins like B12 and vitamin D2 are essential in most hormone pathways. Serum levels of vitamins are determined by blood including levels of antioxidants which are essential in the disposal of toxins and the prevention of disease, such as cancer and dementia. Dietary guidelines always evolve with scientific advances. In a January 2019 article of New England Journal of Medicine November 2018 , a balanced diet includes food within the five groups. A balanced diet maintains good health in menopausal women and reduces the risk of diseases such as diabetes, heart disease, cancer and dementia. An

easy way to follow USDA recommendations is to look at a plate: half should consist of fruits and vegetables and the other half should be made up of grains and proteins. It is recommended that each meal has a serving of low-fat dairy. A micronutrient evaluation will show all of the vitamins, antioxidant levels and minerals present in the white blood cells, thus enabling the practitioner to recognize what is missing from a patient's diet.

3. Begin mindfulness meditation as a way of life practice. The value of the calm spirit enables a strong woman to focus on goals and set intentions for her journey in middle age. Cortisol surges with stress and calming approaches that include yoga, reiki, tai-chi, and other restorative practices. Daily meditation affects the circadian rhythm secretion of high cortisol levels. There is a direct connection of body, mind and spirit.

4. Know the value of other alternative therapies for perimenopause and menopausal women using organic supplements to boost energy libido and help with calmness.

Ashwagandha, rhodiola and cordyceps (calming herbs) assist adrenal dysfunction by regulating production of cortisol during stress.

Turmeric is known for its anti-inflammatory effects and is good for arthritic pain. It is found in yellow ginger common in Asian herbs.

Berberine is a supplement which is essential in prevention of sugar intolerance. It works by blocking sugar absorption and also supports mitochondrial health by activating AMPK (an energy sensor) to regulate energy balance.

Dim (diindolylmethane) is also one of the female supplements that balances hormone metabolism and increases fat-burning with anti-inflammatory effects. It is made from cruciferous vegetables like broccoli and brussels sprouts which balance estrogen and testosterone.

It is recommended for women on hormone replacement therapy. It helps prevent breast and prostate cancer.

Still controversial, cannabinoids are an up and coming source of supplement to assist with issues related to insomnia, neuropathic pain anxiety, migraine headache. The endocannabinoid (ECS) is a biological system based on neurotransmitters binding to receptors. The receptors are found in distribution of the central and peripheral nervous systems. CBD and THC are substances found in cannabinoids and function to regulate the homeostatic role in nutrient transport and insulin sensitivity, including the stress response and behavioral effects on anxiety issues by having a direct effect on the hypothalamic pituitary axis. CBD from hemp and marijuana plants are being used now for treatment of stress disorders like anxiety, post traumatic stress disorder and insomnia.

Paradigm shift in Medicine simply is the future way of taking care of our health.

Here's what symptoms aging women commonly list prior to optimized hormone balancing:
- Anxiety/mood swings/depression

- Lack of sleep, insomnia

- Decreased sex drive or libido

- Weight gain in the belly region

- Hot flashes, night sweats

- Fatigue, lack of energy

- Memory loss, "brain fog"

Here's what women say after they've achieved an optimized body, mind and spirit:

• No more mood swings, stable serene mood

• Increased and improved quality of sleep

• More energy to exercise and work

• Improved sex drive and libido

• Able to lose weight efficiently

• More zest for life

• Greater ability to focus and remember new events

• Feel younger

Overall, a happy life begins with recognizing that each woman has the chance to get the best version of her body, mind and spirit. Menopause can be a new beginning of a new endeavor and a purposeful journey.

ABOUT THE AUTHOR

CYNTHIA MILLS, FASAE, CAE, CMC, CPC, CCRC

Cynthia Mills is The Leaders' Haven Founder, President & CEO; partnering with clients to exceed expectations as business strategist, board consultant, leadership development catalyst, "transformation architect™," executive coach, succession planning Sherpa, change leadership guide, speaker, & facilitator. A multi-award-winning Academy of Leaders CEO & Fellow, Cynthia has authored or contributed to seven books including "The Big Secret" with Jack Canfield of "Chicken Soup for the Soul" renown, for which her chapter "Align for Impact" received an Editor's Choice Award; "CEOs First 90 Days: Breathing Tips for the Other End of the Fire Hose;" and "The Empty Front Porch: Soul Sittin' to Design Your porch to Porch Plan." She is under agreement for eight more books in between traveling the world for clients and enjoying a peaceful wooded haven with her family and friends when home.

Contact:
CynthiaMills@TheLeadersHaven.com
www.TheLeadersHaven.com
www.twitter.com/TheLeadersHaven
www.facebook.com/TheLeadersHaven
www.linkedin.com/in/leadershavenceo

TWO

ENTREPRENEURISM: So You Don't Have to Learn the Hard Way

Cynthia Spraker Mills

BELIEVE
No one ever became a successful entrepreneur who did not believe they could, who saw their unique vision and had the determination to press forward - regardless. The moment we first see a new calling, it's natural to mentally take a figurative step backwards. It's such a breakthrough moment that we can feel the chasm between where we are now and what would be so if this came to pass. Suddenly, for this mirage to flourish, we see how different we must become in relationship to this new prospect having life. We gain a glimpse of the transformation that must occur and the many, many dominoes

that must fall in synchrony. We see the beginning and the dream's fulfillment, forgetting that it's a journey, not a leap. The tapes start flowing. "I don't know how to do this." "I'd have to leave my job." "My family would be very, very nervous." "There are no guarantees." And the really big deterrent - "What if I fail....in front of everyone?"

When your entrepreneurial moment appears, here are substitutes to allow you to feel the joy of creation. "Wow – what an opportunity to learn something new and challenge myself." "This could create the freedom of which I have always dreamed – the chance to lead a team of people to design together, to make a difference, to fundamentally disrupt the way this is done, to solve a problem, to make life easier for others." "While during the developmental stages I might have to put in more time, this idea/product/new company could lead to a lifetime of financial freedom for those I love, to spend my time meaningfully, and to be the catalyst to helping others in ways I had never dreamed." "If this succeeds, it could change, not just my life, but so many others for whom we could create opportunities, and it just might inspire others to become entrepreneurs and follow their dreams!"

If you don't believe:

• The mirage will fade and lose its breath of life.

• Your doubt will be felt by those who could help, and they will not step towards you in co-creation.

• Others may be cheated of the benefit that was theirs if you had acted.

• You may miss out on your life's purpose.

BELIEVE!!

DO YOUR HOMEWORK

Believing is about mindset, determination, consistency, and internal passion, which are the essential baselines necessary for an entrepreneur to stand steady during the journey, particularly when it gets challenging – as it always does. However, a mindset and a belief are not enough to bring a concept to life. Doing our homework involves setting aside the time to complete critical research before we step out.

In our connected world of access, to both information and problems in need of solutions, it is not unusual for more than one person to have a tangential idea that is similar to, or maybe even exactly like, our own. Learning not to be discouraged, to design your differential, and/or to use this new knowledge as a way to uniquely shape your idea(s) are key muscles to build on your journey as an entrepreneur. Having a concept and immediately launching into it, without the appropriate research regarding what already exists or is known to be in development by others, is a businessperson's folly. First steps are as simple as a name search for your business, so that you aren't sued for trademark infringement, or a patent application that reveals your thoughts are not as unique as you would have hoped. We must also protect ourselves and our ideas on the offense. The pursuit of patents, trademarks, and copyright prevent the loss of future proprietary benefits. Failure to do so is not only short-sighted but can be devastating financially and heartbreaking if we lose control of our own creations. Take the time to do these essential pieces of homework.

Before you leave the income security that pays your bills, learning how to run a business is part of your homework. There are government websites specific to each country's requirements for establishing a business, which are important to review before you step out.

Depending upon whether you are becoming a solopreneur - operating without employees, or whether you are planning to build an empire – virtually or with bricks & mortar – this decision will position you very differently as an owner and with your government's expectations. For instance, having employees sets up an entirely different set of legal requirements that you must learn and will require you to have advisor support in order to navigate. While you may start with just yourself, or yourself and a partner, or yourself and one employee; learning what the next steps will need to be as you grow is absolutely important homework before you get to that step. Preparation of this type will allow you to avoid costly mistakes in time and money along the way. It will also help you to design appropriate infrastructure to propel your business forward at key moments, further allowing you to take advantage of strategic opportunities when they present themselves unexpectedly.

As you continue to do your homework, you will find that there is significantly more to put in place at the beginning than you may realize, and it all takes time – more time than you may expect. It is much better to learn first, work through each step and then take your risks than it is to try to launch a new venture, while finalizing a missing foundational business piece. Here is just a partial list to aid you in assessing how much homework you have completed:

- Choose a company name and trademarking filings

- Decide what type of corporate entity and structure under which your company will operate (sole proprietor, partnership, corporation, etc.)

- Set up a separate legal entity so that your personal assets are protected

- Ensure the business interests of your company legally flow into your personal estate upon your death

- Handle all documents related to your death now, including what happens to your business

- Complete all required paperwork in the country, city, county, state, province, or region in which you operate

- Fulfill taxation requirements and reports

- Open a business bank account, comparing fees & services

- Consider whether your customer or your company will pay online fees

- Decide what types of, and how much, insurance protection is needed

- Design a logo

- Select an attorney

- Choose a certified public accountant

- Identify a financial advisor

- Locate a digital guru for your online presence

- Design and manage your online presence (website, social media, YouTube channel, etc.)

- Create regular new content (web, social media, books, newsletter, podcasts, etc.) and set a calendar to do so

- Choose an email service provider & email names that market your enterprise

- Identify your target market(s)

- Create a marketing plan

- Hire, manage, and develop employees

- Develop an appropriate financial management infrastructure

- Select, implement, & manage technology

- Design your strategic framework

- Decide where you need to show up regularly – video, conferences, social media, speeches, TV

- Decide which social media profiles are appropriate, build them, and engage regularly

- Locate a professional photographer & have professional photos taken of you, your product, and your company

There is a voluminous library of books and resources on entrepreneurism. The point of doing your homework is to access them and have an understanding of what it really takes. Realize that the initial phases will consume more time to develop and kick off your undertaking than you think. Plan the plan, and don't walk away from what is currently providing your financial security until you have the foundation in place. Believing is important, and its integral partner is homework.

HAVE A PLAN B

Not every great idea is going to work. Famous inventors and business founders like Thomas Edison and Henry Ford repeatedly went back to the drawing board or experienced company failures. There does come a point after doing our homework when entrepreneurs must step out and take the risk on the investment of time, development, and planning. If you personally have a low risk tolerance for uncertainty or for persistence to see something through, being an entrepreneur might not be the direction for you. However, if you have completed your research, put the components for a successful business in place, and reasonably have assessed that you believe this is where you are meant to be, go for it! What better time than now, and who better to take the risk than you?

That being said, having a Plan B is helpful for those who enter business. Plan B does not have to mean that you're not all in or that you haven't quit your job and aren't working your plan's execution with 100% effort. Plan B can be as simple as, "I have a degree, and I can always go back to "x" to pay the bills if I have to do so." Plan B can be you and a spouse downsizing your lifestyle, so you can live on the other person's income, regardless of whether this venture is successful or not. Plan B can also be, "I'll do this for "x" amount of time, and if we're not seeing this take off, or if we have used "x" dollars from savings at this point, we agree that we gave it a great shot, and it's just not meant to be."

If any of these alternatives make you a little queasy, again reassess whether or not you have what it takes to step out as an entrepreneur. Alternatively, consider whether or not you are comfortable having a bankruptcy in your background, which is the path some business people have repeatedly found themselves in and have been willing to

experience. Remember to also consider those who may be impacted –
for instance children's educations or proximity to retirement years and
whether risking those assets and a lifestyle for both spouses is advisable.
Those who start new ventures tend to be bold, "Why not?" and "What
happens if it works?" people. The uncertainty is the very thing that
propels the entrepreneur forward. Early in my life I had an educational
opportunity that would, in hindsight, serve as the foundation of my
professional life. At that time, I couldn't see myself the way others did,
and my Mom said to me, "Why NOT you?" That fundamentally
changed the way that I looked at every opportunity from that point
forward. So why not you? – AND have a reasonable and sensible Plan
B that you can fall back on without going into financial ruin.

NOT ALL ADVICE IS FOR YOU

Part of the homework and Plan B stages are also having
conversations with people who have gone before you and had both
successes and failures. Sometimes the failures are more important to
hear about than the successes. In some cases, you may be entering
an established field of players, whom you respect and who will be
generous, providing counsel for how to avoid mistakes that they made.
In other cases, you may be creating something that is so uniquely new
to a marketplace that you must be careful about with whom you share
your developing ideas so that your advantage is not lost or stolen.
Regardless, as you get closer and closer to launch, there will be more
people in your orbit who know about what you are going to attempt to
do. It will enable you to ask more questions and gather more targeted
intel from more people. There will also be those who come alongside
you and offer unsolicited advice.

Surprisingly, there will be some who will discourage you, because your risk-taking points out their choices not to follow their entrepreneurial dreams. Notice the source, discount the input when you recognize why it's tainted. Know that their personal pain is appearing and has nothing to do with the soundness of your new venture. Don't discount or reject the person from your life or the fact that there really was good intention in the moment, despite the way it comes across. There will be others, who will be full of joy for you and will encourage you every step of the way. Keep them close, and call upon them when your doubts rise. We are all human, and we all need community in our lives to thrive in business.

Then there will be others, who quite simply just don't get what you are doing or why you are doing it. You may be developing something that has more of a philanthropic under tone and aren't after incredible personal wealth. You may simply enjoy the creation phase of developing and building something new and then are quite happy to sell it and step away for the next idea. Many around you won't understand why you would part from an extraordinarily successful venture, not realizing that it's not the ongoing, day to day implementation that exhilarates you but the design, development, launch, and letting go for the next thing. Their advice to hang on to it and not let go is the very thing that will stifle an entrepreneurial spirit.

Lastly, there are those, whose visions of what you are doing, are in complete misalignment with yours. While they may be very well-intentioned, their counsel could come from fear that if you do all you want to do, it's too much, and it endangers your success. It may be based on a model that has been successful in the past – for many others – but you see that very model as antithetical to what will work in the future, or you believe your new model provides you with a competitive edge. Do you take a risk by following your gut instinct and not listening to those who have gone before you? Perhaps. However, your job as an entrepreneur is to see something new and different and to act on that. It's a discernment exercise to know whether or not others' advice is actually for you. Not all of it is.

When I began publicly sharing my intentions to have my own business, I had more than one well-intentioned businessperson tell me that I MUST select a lane and become "the expert in," "the thought leader of," or "the influencer in," and that to have multiple business lines and to provide multiple services would dilute my brand. As I listened to the counsel, a number of counter thoughts arose for me:

1. I have multiple skills sets and talents to which I would like my clients to have access.

2. I enjoy delivering a wide range of services, which makes me of greater value to my clients and gives me significant professional satisfaction.

3. Having different ways that my clients access me, allows them to become comfortable with the value they receive in one area and builds trust to expand with me into other service areas. This fit with their organizations or businesses allows us to develop a long-term partnership across service lines that reduces their time spent to seek, vet & experience multiple service providers that may or may not work.

4. In difficult economic times, providing a variety of services allows a business to thrive, instead of having a sole service that plummets in demand, causing your company to face financial challenges like lay-offs or pay cuts.

5. Multiple services expand a marketplace beyond one type of client to a broad client base.

6. Choosing to be global instead of local opens up a breadth and depth of learning that stretches me and enhances my ongoing value to all clients. A broader marketplace also protects against economic downturns.

While I absolutely listened intently to all counsel received, ultimately, I chose to go with my business experience, the homework I had done, the strategic framework and foundation I had laid, my broad professional interests, and my gut. When I learned that there is a neurological basis for what we have labeled "gut instinct" and remembered that every time in my life that I have gone against it, I have made big mistakes, I realized that not all advice is for me. I went for my entrepreneurial design, and my choice has been reaffirmed repeatedly – by my clients, by my experiences, by my business satisfaction, and financially.

HAVE FAITH: THE RESOURCES WILL APPEAR

While I had decades of business experience when I stepped out on my own, there were many things that I did not know how to do: build the back end of a website, discern which social media channels to engage and why, write a book, choose a publisher, file all the paperwork to own a business, what order everything needed to be done in, which taxes I would be subject to, how to design a logo without considerable expense, and on and on it goes.

What became amazing to me over time was how often exactly what I needed showed up in the moment. For instance, I received a call from someone who had been told that before they spoke on a particular topic, they should call me as an expert in this arena and have a conversation. That led to a new friendship, most importantly, and also a connection to a terrific digital guru, whose company doesn't just design sites but is a partner in building your entire online presence. They subsequently helped me with some of the items on my initial homework list, including creating an overall marketing strategy.

One of the most important characteristics of an entrepreneur is to have faith – that you are enough, that you do not have to know everything, and that the right resources, contacts, and opportunities will present themselves when you are ready for them. It has happened over and over and over again on my journey. Have faith: the resources WILL appear.

IT MATTERS WITH WHOM YOU DO BUSINESS

When we're children, our parents create guard rails for us, regarding with whom they are comfortable that we spend time. They know the influences that others can have on malleable minds, the power of experiences, and that key connections will bring others to us, who will either enhance our lives or can destroy them in a moment.

Business is no different. It absolutely matters with whom you do business. Not all customers are yours, and not all providers of services you will need as a business owner are people with whom you will want to be affiliated. I remember a key moment when I was leading an organization that was in growth mode. During a board meeting, the director emphasized that we did not want to close every potential lead. At the time, I was completely puzzled given the pressure that the board of directors was putting on our team to achieve our growth targets.

Over time, I listened to the business owners share their experiences of disastrous customer experiences – some that just chewed up way too much time in terms of unreasonable demands, some who kept expanding the scope of services but didn't expect the cost for those services to expand with them, and others who chose to file lawsuits. I began to gain an enhanced understanding, regarding what it means to not want every customer.

The underpinning for peace with whom you do business is to have clarity around your company's values and your personal values. When you find yourself tempted to do business with people or companies who don't share your framework for life and business, or about whom you would be uncomfortable sharing on social media that they are a customer or vendor to you, remind yourself, "not every customer is yours," and "it matters with whom you do business."

ECONOMIC EBBS & FLOWS – PLAN FOR THEM

With normal economic cycles running somewhere around five years in recent times up until the Great Recession, business owners know to expect periods of expansion and contraction. Entrepreneurs must think carefully about timing of the launch of new ventures. On the one hand, when capital and access to it are least expensive and easily acquired, jumping on that opportunity is advisable. On the other hand, when one sees the likelihood of a recession looming, timing in launching a product that is dependent upon consumers' disposable income is a critical consideration.

The smart entrepreneur thinks like a real estate agent. Sometimes the market is flooded with buyers, but the housing inventory is not there, so regardless of buyer desire, the ability to make a high number of sales is impossible for the agent. Other times, the inventory is high, but the economic conditions are such that the buyer pool is low. The smart real estate agent doesn't live to their highest total income annually but plans for the subsequent lean years when the balance of buyers and inventory aren't in alignment. Business owners who survived the great recession weren't as highly leveraged with debt. They already operated more leanly so their profit margins were high in good times, which also carried them in bad times.

Astute entrepreneurs follow the business cycles and understand the risks of a new launch, or even leveraging into a growth mode that requires acquiring more debt. They expect that there will be times when business is not as robust. When leading a business before the great recession, I remember the day when something just didn't feel right. I couldn't put my finger on it, but I knew that what we had been experiencing as normal was beginning to feel like it could go sideways. I wrote a multi-year plan for contraction with multiple worst-case scenarios and presented it to my leadership partners. It wound up being the best investment of time I could have ever made. The plans were formulated from an "if this, then that" framework, so that if I saw certain variables appear, I would pre-empt the problem by taking related specific actions. By the time the Great Recession had fully reared its head, I had executed all plans and all facets of each plan. It was that foresight that allowed us to survive and thrive. Entrepreneurs know that economic ebbs and flows will happen – plan for them and you too will survive and thrive!

BOARD OF ADVISORS

No one gets anywhere on their own, and this is never truer than the decision to become an entrepreneur. Yes, you will need to identify a business/corporate attorney, a CPA, a financial planner, an insurance broker, a digital guru, a technology contractor, a business coach, maybe a venture capitalist (VC), and etc. These are your vendors, who are your partners in your business' success, and upon whom you will call at various stages of development.

However, there is a less formal and less official group that you need to develop and that is your Board of Advisors. This is not a legally and fiduciarily responsible company Board of Directors. Your Board of Advisors is the group of people, whom you have identified are for YOU! They may have different business or technical skills and may overlap some of the vendors you have chosen, and yet, not necessarily so. These people are your champions! They know you. They will tell you the truth. They may have key connections for you. You can turn to them when you are struggling. There should be no risk in sharing your personal or business vulnerabilities or doubts. Examples of the types of people you might want to have on your Board of Advisors include: your spiritual advisor, a parent, a best friend, a business associate from the community, the chair of the local business association, and someone who does the same thing as you but does not compete in your market and never will. This is not a group of people you convene together, but the group of people whom you can call upon, depending upon the circumstances in which you find yourself.

Being an entrepreneur is exciting, exhilarating, and at times scary, particularly at the point at which you see something that no one else can yet. Being able to step away from those who are counting on you for their livelihood, or the public nature of what you have launched to the world on social media, or the pressures of owning your own business; in order to have the insights and perspectives of people whom you can trust and lean upon, is an important element of being successful. It is also the sign of a mature leader.

FINAL ENTREPRENEURIAL TIPS

With only the luxury of a chapter's length, here are a few concluding tips for new entrepreneurs

You Can't Do It All: As your business takes off, bring in those who can help you, outsource what you can, think virtually for hires before going to bricks and mortar to open up your talent pool, and stay as lean as you can. Don't make the mistake of trying to do it all. Your business needs not just your initial idea but your strategic leadership. Remember to work on your business and that includes working on yourself as a leader. The more you become a people developer, the more your business will prosper, and the burden of doing can be removed from you, so that you can lead and co-create most of the time.

Show Up Or You're Not in the Game: You can have the best product in the world or be the best consultant in the world, but if you don't show up, in today's business world, you are forgotten. <u>BE EVERYWHERE</u>: This means social media, video including a YouTube channel, streaming live, speaking at conferences and local events, creating podcasts, TV and radio interviews, blogs, emailed newsletters, trade and professional magazine columns, website, books and much more. Regardless of how many likes, views, or emails after your speeches, people are noticing and seeing you. Even if they hit the delete button, they momentarily were made aware of you and your product or service above the din of way too much content being pushed to all of us. You must get above the noise through what is termed today, "everywhere marketing." When you hear, "you are EVERYWHERE," you will know that the market strategy you have deployed is gaining traction. Does all of this take time when you are a new entrepreneur – absolutely. Is it critical for you to figure out how to participate, deploy, time, and outsource your strategy? Absolutely. Your competition will if you don't – so show up, or you're not in the game.

New Business Resources: You absolutely must be involved in at least one, and preferably many, business and professional communities. There are professional associations, small business associations, local business groups or chambers of commerce, consulting associations, and trade associations for every type of business around the world. Find one that has people you enjoy, resources you need, and participate. Your competitors are, so don't miss out on the community and the opportunities waiting to help entrepreneurs. You may also want to take advantage of hiring a business or executive coach. You can do this by identifying independent coaches, who work with business owners and developing entrepreneurs. If you want to meet in person, do a local Google search, but many successful coaches work with clients all over the world and don't ever sit face to face. You may also want to consider Vistage or C-12 – both organizations that provide key business resources for business owners from different perspectives.

Read, Read, Read: Entrepreneurs must know what is going on, not just in their immediate competitive arena, but what is happening in every facet that could impact their product or service. This means keeping up with political and economic cycles, changes to laws and regulations, understanding developing technologies that could be disruptors, learning how to maximize the strengths of each generation within your employees, and learning from the successes and failures of other business leaders, industries, and professions. Becoming a voracious reader is a key characteristic of successful entrepreneurs. It's also the fastest way to identify the next gap or problem to solve that just might kick off your next entrepreneurial adventure.

People: Remember that any success you have will be built with other people, most of whom will show up to work every day wanting to contribute meaningfully, have satisfaction of a job well done at the end of the day, would like to learn something new, want to be trusted, and would be thrilled to know how they could grow with your company. When mistakes happen, as they will, remember that most of your team did not show up that morning wondering how they could mess up, frustrate you, slow down the launch, or make your life difficult. Usually, there is a gap in a process, poor training, a failure to transfer knowledge, incomplete communication, or unclear expectations at the root of the problem – all of which can be fixed and none of which are about "bad employees." Remember as a new entrepreneur, "We manage processes. We lead people." Spend your time developing your people, and they will engineer out the bad processes and communications issues, because they want to be part of a success story just as much as you do. Give them the chance to co-lead with you, and watch how many times they exceed your expectations.

Have FUN!: I was once being selected to lead an organization as the new CEO, and the Chair of the Board, who was on the phone with the CFO, overheard a lot of laughter in the background. The CFO said to me, "The Chair wants to know if you come on board whether there is going to be this much laughter going on every day?" I replied, "If I'm going to spend more time here with this team than I do with my family, I fully expect there to be a lot of laugher amongst us every day!!" Choosing to become an entrepreneur is a significant commitment, and yet, it's never not about the people with whom we choose to engage – whether they be employees, customers/clients, or vendors to our company or organization. How we choose to be as leaders will set the tone, and having fun with what we're all attempting to launch together releases a creativity and creates an atmosphere that fosters continual trust and new ideas. Enjoy the decision you have made. Share the excitement with others, and allow them to have fun designing and implementing a transformational future with everyone.

As you ponder becoming an entrepreneur, if you can choose to fully believe, do your homework, have a Plan B, remember that not all advice is for you, have faith that the resources will appear, act from an understanding that it matters with whom you do business, plan for economic ebbs & flows, carefully select a board of advisors, recognize that you can't do it all, show up and be in the game, exploit every business resource you can identify, read everything, focus on your people, and have fun – absolutely everything that you put into becoming an entrepreneur will be worth every minute! I can't wait to hear about your business' launch!

ABOUT THE AUTHOR

MARY OUCHIE

Mary Ouchie is a contributing author of Professional Women's Network anthologies, *Total Woman and Finding Your Voice. Total Woman's* chapter, *A Compromising Position* demonstrates the art of compromise. In *Finding Your Voice,* her chapter, *Lost In A Fog,* provides an inside look of her family's experience with Alzheimer's disease as well as warning signs and tips for prevention and care for someone with Alzheimer's.

Mary Ouchie is a children's book author and illustrator. Her first book, *Grandma Forgot My Name* is a story of a grandparent with Alzheimer's disease. The story gently shows what happens to the brain with Alzheimer's disease and how to help recover some memories. This is Mary Ouchie's first children's book receiving a prestige Professional Woman's Network award. Mary Ouchie also provided the beautiful illustrations for *Grandma Forgot My Name.* Her illustrations were made in art quilt form using vibrant colors of fabrics to show a loving family in the story.

Twirly Girl, Mary Ouchie's second children's book, a girl with Autism tells her experiences through the eyes of Autism and she discovers her talent that she already possessed. Her illustrations using fiber arts, shows us the world of Autism.

Foster Kid, told by a man looking back on his foster care experience is Mary Ouchie's third children's book with Professional Woman's Network. Ouchie's illustrations show the characters with all skin tones and hair colors to represent foster care of all people.

Mary Ouchie graduated from the University of Wisconsin-Milwaukee with a degree in Educational Studies and UWM's Interpreter Training Program. Mary has worked as an Educational Interpreter in various schools in Wisconsin and as a teacher's assistant with students in Special Education.

Mary lives with her lovingly devoted husband, Don in Menomonee Falls, WI. She has two creative and handsome grown sons, Chris and Nick along with his wife, Megan (Stew).

Contact:
Email: maryouchie@gmail.com
Website: LovingMemoriesBooks.com

THREE

A Compromising Position

Mary Ouchie

In today's society compromising is given a negative connotation. Never give in. Don't be a pushover. Don't get taken advantage of. Get the better of the deal. Lowball the offer. Always to be the winner and let them lose. No one wants to be put into a compromising position. It makes you vulnerable to embarrassment and shows you in an incriminating situation. No one meets in the middle anymore. We see it all around our country these days in politics, business, sports, and in everyday living.

The word compromise itself is comprised of the prefix **com** -meaning with or together or in common and the word **promise** - an assurance that something to be given. In other words, to have a common or mutual assurance that something is to be given to each other.

A compromise is a shared mindset given as a kindness to benefit one another.

If the true meaning of compromise consists to be beneficial for all; how did we get to this point of negativity? The German word, schadenfreude may give us some insight to the stem of negativity.

"Schadenfreude is the experience of pleasure, joy, or self-satisfaction that comes from learning of or witnessing the troubles, failures, or humiliation of another." (Wikipedia)

It is not difficult to look around our society to see schadenfreude in action. Check out YouTube, America's Funniest Videos, video games and any streaming or televised show, our politics to see some form of schadenfreude. How did we get here? Why has it become pleasurable to see someone else's misfortune?

In years past before the Internet and the deluge of social media, we had a simpler world. We lived closer to our families. We knew the people in our neighborhoods and our places of worship. We lived in smaller circles than we do now. We watched out for each other, took time to talk over our fences. We were a part of a community.

Our families were larger with several children in close spaces. Living in close quarters lends itself to compromise. Everyone needs the bathroom, the telephone, the car etc. at the same time. The only way to make living work was through compromise. Everyone needed to give in a little to get something in return. It was a time we practiced compromising in our everyday life.

Civility or to be polite to others is not as common these days. There used to be a time whenever you were accidently bumped into both people said they are sorry; even if it wasn't their fault. Now in the same situation the bumper blames the bumpee for just being there in their way. Where has civility gone?

Our society is suffering from growing pains. We live farther and farther from our families. We live in a more isolated life in larger communities where you don't know all your neighbors. Our lives are busier with our jobs, and our kids' activities to really connect face to face with others. Our connection to family and friends are through social media outlets. We've become more separated from one another. The need for civility and compromise has gone to the wayside because we are not bumping into one another's lives as we were before. We are out of practice.

Let us explore the art to of compromise. Unlike schadenfreude where you enjoy to see others hurt or embarrassed, try to put yourself in the other's shoe or viewpoint. In doing so, doesn't mean you have to agree with their view or compromise your moral outlook. It just means you need to find an understanding of their viewpoint. Once you get to a place where you can comprehend their side and try to understand them; it is time to a find middle ground where you both can agree and /or find mutual respect for your differing opinions.

To begin the practice of compromise it is imperative to have the ability to listen and understand both sides of a conflict. Here is an example issue to begin our practice.

In America there has been a huge controversy over Colin Kaepernick, a football player in the National Football League (NFL), taking a knee as a protest during the National Anthem. Now just for the sake of narrowing down the viewpoints let us not include politics and the NFL in the equation. Let us focus on the Colin Kaepernick's Black Lives Matter protest and the Military's view of the protest showing disrespect to the flag. Again this is a practice of looking into both sides of an issue, not to compromise your moral outlook. We are just exploring our mutual respect for one another's viewpoint.

"Compromise, contrary to popular opinion, does not mean selling out one's principles. Compromise means working out differences to forge a solution..." —Madeleine M. Kunin

The United States Military has a strong connection to our flag and the National Anthem. It represents the country that they serve to protect, have left their homes and families, have been injured and have died all for the devotion and honor to serve and protect our country. The flag represents to them their sacrifices and it is an integral part of their lives. If you have ever witnessed a flag ceremony at a military funeral or a military event you would recognize the importance. At a funeral the casket is draped with the US flag. Through the formal ceremony of the flag the military representatives fold the flag thirteen times. There are differences in the symbols of the folds by the different sectors of the military. Here is one example:

1. *The first fold of our flag is a symbol of life.*

2. *The second fold signifies our belief in eternal life.*

3. *The third fold is made in honor and tribute of the veteran departing our ranks, and who gave a portion of his or her life for the defense of our country to attain peace.*

4. *The fourth fold exemplifies our weaker nature as citizens trusting in God; it is to Him we turn for His divine guidance.*

5. *The fifth fold is an acknowledgment to our country, for in the words of Stephen Decatur, "Our country, in dealing with other countries, may she always be right, but it is still our country, right or wrong."*

6. *The sixth fold is for where our hearts lie. It is with our heart that we pledge allegiance to the flag of the United States of America, and to the republic for which it stands, one nation under God, indivisible, with liberty and justice for all.*

7. *The seventh fold is a tribute to our armed forces, for it is through the armed forces that we protect our country and our flag against all enemies.*

8. *The eighth fold is a tribute to the one who entered into the valley of the shadow of death, that we might see the light of day, and to honor our mother, for whom it flies on Mother's Day.*

9. *The ninth fold is an honor to womanhood, for it has been through their faith, love, loyalty, and devotion that the character of the men and women who have made this country great have been molded.*

10. *The 10th fold is a tribute to father, for he, too, has given his sons and daughters for the defense of our country since he or she was first-born.*

11. *The 11th fold, in the eyes of Hebrew citizens, represents the lower portion of the seal of King David and King Solomon and glorifies, in their eyes, the God of Abraham, Isaac, and Jacob.*

12. *The 12th fold, in the eyes of a Christian citizen, represents an emblem of eternity and glorifies, in their eyes, God the Father, the Son, and Holy Ghost.*

13. *The last fold, when the flag is completely folded, the stars are uppermost, reminding us of our national motto, "In God We Trust." (The symbolism of the 13 folds of the U.S. Flag https://alaforveterans. wordpress.com/2017/06/16/the-symbolism-of-the-13-folds-of-the-u-s-flag/ 10-21-18)*

The flag along with the National Anthem are sacred symbols to be respected with standing to honor the country that they have long sacrificed to protect us all.

"Tolerance, compromise, understanding, acceptance, patience - I want those all to be very sharp tools in my shed." —CeeLo Green

There has been a long history of discrimination of African Americans in our country. During the year 2014, a white neighborhood watchman shot a young black unarmed teenager named, Trayvon Martin. That man was not charged in the shooting and that began the Black Lives Matter movement.

Later that same year, Eric Garner, an African American, was killed while being arrested for suspicion of selling single cigarettes. He was put into a chokehold and he called out that he could not breathe. The police did call for an ambulance for him, but CPR was not given to him because they believed he was breathing. One hour later, Garner died. The medical examiner declared it a homicide. The police officer was not indicted. Quickly the Black Lives Matter movement began to evolve against police brutality. The following month, Michael Brown another unarmed black teenager was shot 6 times by a white police officer. That officer too was not indicted for the shooting. This incident propelled the strong emotions for the Black Lives Matter movement. In 2015, there were more shootings of African Americans by police demonstrating the importance to show America the prejudices and brutality by police departments in our nation.

Colin Kaepernick, an African American football player in the NFL, began to support the movement Black Lives Matter with a quiet protest sitting on the bench during the National Anthem. Other NFL players joined him as he gain support from his fellow players.

An US Army veteran, Nate Boyer, got in contact with Kaepernick to discuss his protest sitting out during the National Anthem. Boyer was outraged by his actions. As they discussed the issue together, Boyer asked if Kaepernick would consider taking a knee in a form of prayer as when a soldier visits a grave of a fallen soldier. Boyer felt it would be more respectful than sitting on the bench. Kaepernick agreed to the compromise to show more respect by kneeling as a sign of prayer. (YouTube Why Colin Kaepernick Took a Knee (US Army Veteran, Nate Boyer)

This is the gist of both sides of the situation. Do you have a better understanding or compassion for the other side of the issue? You don't have to agree with either side, but it is important to see the other's side with some understanding and empathy.

Knowing both sides enlightens you to see how others think and act. Information and compassion are tools towards compromise.

"A compromise is the art of dividing a cake in such a way that everyone believes he has the biggest piece." —Ludwig Erhard

Your Thoughts
What makes a good compromise?

_____

_____

_____

How can you put yourself into others shoes?

_____

_____

_____

Is it difficult to see another's point of view?

_____

_____

_____

Middle children characteristics: patience, ability to see both sides of situations, giving in for the greater good, empathy, tolerance, and accommodating.

What happened to the middle children?

_____

_____

_____

Are born negotiators extinct?

_____

_____

_____

Are we missing something valuable in middle children?

_____

_____

_____

Compromise quiz
1. In traffic:

    A.   You allow cars to merge into your lane.

    B.   You inch closer to the car ahead not allowing cars in.

    C.   You allow one car in but that is all.

2. While Shopping:

    A.   You allow customers with a small amount of groceries to go ahead of you.

    B.   First come first serve.

    C.   You are in a hurry; you can't let others go ahead.

3. While working on a group project:

    A.   You listen to others thoughts on how to proceed and choose the majority idea.

    B.   You make all the decisions

    C.   Listen to all ideas but you choose your idea.

4. While picking up a meal for your family you:

    A. You listen to the family's choices and pick the choice of the majority.

    B. You make the decision for your family.

    C. You stop and get all the different food choices your family wants.

5. You are invited to go to the movies to see a movie of their choosing on a day that you have business to do. You:

    A. You negotiate a time that works out for both of you.

    B. You agree to go along, but you choose the movie.

    C. You go to the movies, but do your business during the movie.

If you tended to select the *A* answers you are the great compromiser. You tend to give a little and you get a little in return.

If you chose the *B* answers you are someone who needs to take control and are not comfortable with compromise.

If you are someone who chose the *C* answers you maybe someone who gives too much or you are someone you would like to compromise but likes to have the final say.

"A good compromise, ...is like a good sentence; or a good piece of music. Everybody can recognize it. They say, 'Huh. It works. It makes sense.' " —Barack Obama

Practice the art compromising in small steps. These little acts of kindness are little compromises shown to others in a day. Have you experienced acts of kindness like the following?

- Someone let you go ahead of him or her in line.

- Held the door open for you.

- Gave you a smile.

- Helped you pick up things that you dropped.

- Someone sacrificed his or her time to benefit you.

How did these experiences mean to you? Sharing in civility towards others gives us the compassion needed to compromise. Our society is changing, but in the end it is up to us to keep our values, civility, compassion for others, meet in the middle and compromise.

"My own experience is use the tools that are out there.
Use the digital world. But never lose sight of the need to reach out and
talk to other people who don't share your view. Listen to them and see if
you can find a way to compromise." —Colin Powell

Compromise has been a part of me through my growing years as a middle child. Actually I share the middle with my older brother, as we are the third and fourth child out of six children. Interestingly we are similar in personality. As a child in the middle of a family you learn quickly to be a team player. In a large family taking turns is commonplace. Giving up on things you want for the greater good of all the family was expected. You knew eventually that it would be your turn to benefit. That is the way in big families- you give a little, you get a little.

In being a middle of a family, I grew up naturally able to be a listener as my words were often drowned out by my older and younger siblings. So I developed a way to be heard, I would wait them out and then speak my peace. Waiting and being patient was how I lived my life.

My work life used my experiences as a middle child as I worked as a nursing assistant, group home relief parent, an educational sign language interpreter, real estate agent, a teaching assistant and many other positions including writing and illustrating children's books. All these positions put me in the listening position and the go between people.

A hand-stitched illustration created for this international book called *Diversity by Mary Ouchie*

References

https://www.brainyquote.com/quotes/madeleine_m_kunin_549657?src=t_

compromise https://www.vocabulary.com/dictionary/compromising

Schadenfreude Wikipedia(google Sept.15,2018)

http://www.huffingtonpost.com/charlene-haparimwi/why-the-ph

youtubeWhy Colin Kaepernick Took a Knee (US Army Veteran, Nate Boyer)

rase-all-lives-_b_9760604.html?utm_hp_ref=black-voices

Black Lives Matter

The symbolism of the 13 folds of the U.S. Flag   https://alaforveterans.wordpress.com/2017/06/16/the-symbolism-of-the-13-folds-of-the-u-s-flag/ 10-21-18

https://www.brainyquote.com/quotes/barack_obama_375647?src=t_compromise

https://www.brainyquote.com/quotes/colin_powell_446000?src=t_compromise

ABOUT THE AUTHOR

MARGARET BECK

Margaret "Peg" Beck, SPHR, SHRM-SCP, is a nationally certified senior human resources professional who brings over 25 years of experience as chief human resources officer providing strategic and operational oversight in both the public and private sector. Currently she is Co-consultant and owner with her husband of a management consulting firm, Creative Consulting Associates, LLC, a former professor of graduate studies in Leadership/Management and Human Resources Management, PWN Certified Leadership Coach, seminar leader, conference speaker, workshop facilitator and author.

Her publications include Life Lessons: A passport for personal & professional success, co-author for the Female Architect: How to Rebuild Your Life and the Female Factor: A Confidence Guide for Women.

She earned her MBA from Nova Southeastern University, Ft. Lauderdale, Florida. And is nationally certified as a Senior Professional in Human Resources (SPHR), and SHRM Senior Certified Professional, (SHRM-SCP), Certified Leadership Coach, PWN, and a certified trainer for Developmental Dimensions International.

She has been honored as Human Resource Professional of the Year, by the State Council of Florida, and the NISOD Excellence Award by the National Institute of Staff and Organizational Development, Austin, TX, and has served on many boards including the International Advisory Board of PWN.

Contact:
Peg Beck
Creative Consulting Associates
6522 43rd Court E.
Sarasota, FL 34243
pzbeck@gmail.com
(941) 387-6292
Facebook: Life Lessons: A passport for personal & professional success

FOUR

Leaders in Pearls

Margaret Beck

What's in a name? What images does "Leaders in Pearls" bring up to you? Initially, it made me think of the '50's image of women secretaries in high heels, dresses and pearls. A stereotype I didn't like! This was a time when there were few job opportunities for women, let alone positions in leadership.

Then I thought about a pearl. How does this beautiful jewel get created from a piece of sand or food in the oyster? A natural pearl is formed when the oyster overcomes the "intruder" by covering the uninvited visitor with layers of nacre — the mineral substance that fashions the oyster's shells. Layer upon layer of nacre, also known as mother-of-pearl, coat the grain of sand until the iridescent gem is formed.

Cultured pearls are made in the same way. The only difference is that instead of accidental circumstances, a "pearl farmer" embeds a grain of sand into the mollusk.
—Live Science, Life's Mysteries, How do Oysters make pearls, Michelle Bryner, November 20, 2012

Saltwater pearls may take 5 to 20 years to grow. The longer a pearl stays in the shell, the more nacre that forms and the larger and usually more expensive the pearl.

As I thought more about it, I realized that we are all **Leaders in Pearls.** Just as valuable pearls are created from an obstacle, so have women in leadership developed through overcoming obstacles. I came to love the title "Leaders in Pearls" and wear them with great pride and new significance.

The oyster overcoming the sand reminds me of the struggles woman had to overcome in their fight for equality – from the earliest centuries to the current day. Many women have fought hard as leaders in their respective fields so that we can have the opportunities we have today. Whether it is the right to vote, job opportunities, membership in Congress, or as leaders in various professions, we all stand on their shoulders.

This year marks the Centennial of the passage of the 19th Amendment to the Constitution of the United States. Passed by Congress **June 4, 1919**, and ratified on **August 18, 1920**, the 19th amendment granting women the right to vote. First brought up to

Congress on January 10, 1878, it took **41 years**, bringing it up every year until it was finally approved by Congress. It was finally ratified by the required 75% of the states on August 18, 1920 with Tennessee being the state to cast the final approval vote. The last state to ratify it was Mississippi on March 22, 1984, so it was more than a 100-year fight before every state agreed that all women had the right to vote! What a fight and sacrifice our sisters before us made!

Recently I read a book "Bad Girls throughout History: 100 Remarkable Women Who Changed the World," by Ann Shen. The stories date back to the Garden of Eden, where, in certain mystical texts Lilith was the first wife of Adam. She refused to be subservient and was cast out of the Garden. She was represented as the demon in mystical writings and was never mentioned in the Bible. Now she is really a "bad-ass" to be kicked out of the Bible because she believed she should be equal! Abigail Adams, the second First Lady, was a true equal to her husband, John Adams our second president. She read all his speeches and formal documents before he delivered them. She was so politically active that people often referred to her as "Mrs. President."

More recent women described in her book were firsts in many industries:

• Sally Ride, first woman and youngest person in space.

• Oprah, who was fired from her first evening news reporter job for being "too emotional", to owning her own network and America's first female self-made billionaire;

• Madonna, widely considered one of the most influential musicians and best-selling solo female recording artist of all time;

- Tina Fey, the first female head writer in SNL's history, and finally,

- Malala Yousfzai, the seventeen-year-old Pakistani activist for women's education. On October 9, 2012, a fatwa (Islamic religious decree) was issued against her by the Taliban and she was shot in the head by a masked Taliban gunman while she was riding home from school. She survived the assassination attempt, and after several months of recovery became an international advocate and speaker for children's rights to education. Her incredible courage inspired the world to act; the UN passed a petition in her name that led to the Pakistan's ratifying its first Right to Education Bill. At seventeen, she became the youngest Nobel Peace Prize winner and on her 18th birthday she used the money raised to open a school in Lebanon for Syrian refugees. She truly is one "bad-ass" young girl!

    Why do I tell you these stories?? I believe it is because of these women who have come before us, fighting for women's rights and leading the way to the liberties and chances we have now to be "Leaders in Pearls."

Recent Successes for Women
    These former trail blazers led the way for the women who have led some of our recent successes. Following are just a few of them:

➤ **Gains in the United States Congress**
    In the mid-term election in November 2018, 102 women were elected to the United States House of Representatives and 15 were elected to the Senate. Of the women elected, 36 were first time members of Congress. All together there are now 127 women, about

25% of the members of Congress. <u>According to the Washington Post</u>, not only did 2018 see a huge jump in women candidates, it also saw a massive bump in the number of women who were vying for their first-ever elected office.

The gains last year mirror those that took place in 1992, <u>the other renowned "Year of the Woman,"</u> when **four** women were elected to the Senate and **24** women were elected to the House. In the follow-up to the 1992 election, it appeared to <u>reaffirm research</u> suggesting that the election of women has a notable impact on policies that are raised. In the wake of the 1992 election, Congress passed the Family and Medical Leave Act as well as the Violence Against Women Act.

➤ #Me Too Movement

The #Me Too Movement which began to raise the consciousness and outcry against sexual harassment and violence against women, celebrated its one-year anniversary on October 15, 2018. The movement has dislodged scores of men from their high-powered positions and sparked a national conversation about workplace sexual harassment.

Although it was originally started by Tarana Burke, an African-American activist, more than 10 years ago, it was set ablaze after a tweet by actress Alyssa Milano who wrote: "If you've been sexually harassed or assaulted write 'me too' as a reply to this tweet."

So, just how popular has the hashtag become? A recent study by the Pew Research Center found that the #MeToo hashtag was used more than 19 million times on Twitter since Milano's initial tweet. That's more than 55,000 uses of the hashtag per day. - USA Today, October 13, 2018.

➤ **The Women's March, on January 21, 2017**

The Women's March was organized to support <u>gender equality</u> and <u>civil rights</u>. The march was initially scheduled to be held only in Washington, <u>D.C.</u>, but "sister marches" arose throughout the United States and numerous other countries. and it was widely believed to be the largest single-day demonstration in our country's history.

According to organizers, more than 670 events were held on seven continents. It was believed that between 3.3 million and 4.6 million people attended the marches in the United States, while worldwide participation was reported to be about 5 million. The central demonstration in Washington, D.C., estimates swelled to from 500,000 to 1 million people according to the crowd estimate study by Jeremy Pressman, (University of Connecticut) and Erica Chenowith, (University of Denver).

There's Still a Long Way to Go

There is still bleak news for women in top leadership positions in most industries. Below are just a few releases of data since 2017.

The 360 Law Glass Ceiling Report released in May 2018, surveyed over 300 law firms. The report showed that women made up over 40 percent of law school students for more than three decades, and now make up more than half, according to the American Bar Association (ABA). Women continue to be underrepresented at all levels of a typical law firm. It found that at no level has the representation of women non-partners, partners or equity partners increased by more than a percentage point from the previous year.

Women were just over 35 percent of all attorneys surveyed, meaning that men still constitute almost two-thirds of private practice.

Women account for only 21 percent of equity partners and 12 percent of the highest firm leadership roles. In addition, ABA data shows that minority women made up almost one-fifth of the first-year law students in 2017. Yet they currently represent only 8 percent of private practice attorneys and 3 percent of all partners.

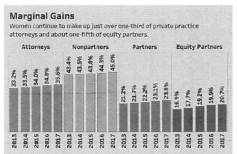

Marginal Gains
Women continue to make up just over one-third of private practice attorneys and about one-fifth of equity partners.

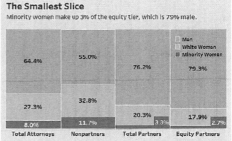

The Smallest Slice
Minority women make up 3% of the equity tier, which is 79% male.

➤ Women CEOs at hospitals

According to an article in Becker's Hospital Review (Kelly Gooch, Monday, January 14th, 2019) women continue to be under represented in the healthcare C-Suite (chief officers).

While women play a large role in the healthcare workforce, they are missing from hospital leadership positions. For the report, researchers identified and developed profiles of more than 3,000 C-suite executives and board members and analyzed the career paths of 112 CEOs. They also interviewed more than 75 men and women in healthcare — from directors to CEOs — about the dynamics women face in the industry.

Here are five findings of the report:

1. Women consumers make 80 percent of buying and usage decisions in healthcare and represent 65 percent of the industry workforce.

2. While women have influence in healthcare, researchers found they only represent 25 percent to 35 percent of industry C-suite teams and 13 percent of industry CEOs.

3. Researchers found it is more difficult for women to achieve the same level of implicit trust in male-dominated workplaces. "The closer you get to the top, the less diversity exists, and the more dominant male perceptions and associated biases become," they concluded. "When women do make it to roles reporting to the CEO, they tend to serve as technical experts [such as chief human resources officer, chief legal officer, CIO]."

4. On average, it takes women three to five years longer than men to reach CEO, depending on the organization.

5. 86 percent of payer and provider CEOs had prior profit-and-loss experience, but men are three times more likely to have P&L positions.

➤ Women College or University Presidents and CEO's of Corporate America

According to the 2017 American College President Survey conducted by the American Council on Education, women comprised only 30% of college presidents across the country based on numbers reported for 2016. Women of color make up a mere 5% of college presidents. Why are there so few women at the top of the Ivory Tower?

Some variables that account for a lack of women in leadership roles include a lack of diversity in hiring practices, bias, and family life. Bristol Community College President Laura Douglas told the Boston Globe a lack of diversity on boards that hire presidents is one contributing factor. Some may not have much experience working with women leaders as senior executives, and they're going to choose those with whom they're comfortable.

Andrea Silbert, the president of Massachusetts-based Eos Foundation, which has conducted research into the lack of women leaders in higher education, told Newsweek it is an issue of bias: "There's a lot of unconscious bias against women being the No. 1 at the top, whether that's the president of the United States, a governor or the president of a college."

Family life may be another factor that prevents women from climbing to the rank of the presidency, according to a study conducted at the University of California at Berkley. The study found that working women with children are less likely to earn tenure-track positions, compared to their male peers. Researchers dubbed this "the baby penalty." Similarly, the American College President Survey found that 32% of women had "altered career progression to care for others" compared to 16% of male survey respondents.

While women are underrepresented among university presidential ranks, higher ed places more females in top executive roles than corporate America, by a significant margin. According to a Pew Research Center study released in April, women comprise only 5% of CEOs based on an analysis of federal security filings by 1,500 companies.

Comparatively speaking, more women are leading institutions of higher learning than ever before, with a jump from 10% in 1986 to 30% in 2016.

"While we would like to see numbers reflect more progress in certain areas," Molly Corbett Broad, the council's president until late 2017, told The New York Times, "I do believe that the needle is slowly moving in the right direction."

https://www.forbes.com/sites/joshmoody/2018/07/05/where-are-all-the-female-college-presidents/

The narrowing, but persistent, gender gap in pay

The gender gap in pay has narrowed since 1980 but has remained relatively stable over the past 15 years. In 2018, women earned 85% of what men earned, according to a Pew Research Center analysis of median hourly earnings of both full- and part-time workers in the United States. The Census Bureau found that, in 2017, full-time, year-round working women earned 80% of the earnings of their male counterparts. The 2018 wage gap was somewhat smaller for adults ages 25 to 34 than for all workers, with the women ages 25 to 34 earning 89 cents for every dollar a man in the same age group earned.

The gender pay gap is narrower among young adults than among workers overall

Median hourly earnings of U.S. women as percentage of men's median among ...

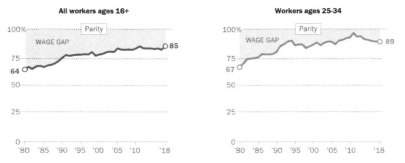

Note: Estimates are for civilian, non-institutionalized, full- or part-time employed workers with positive earnings. Self-employed workers are excluded.
Source: Pew Research Center analysis of Current Population Survey data.

PEW RESEARCH CENTER

The good news is, that there ARE more women in leadership positions, more women with college degrees, more women attorneys, and more women in Congress. We place our trust with our younger sisters to continue this march toward equality.

Qualities of Successful Leaders

In Chapter 9, Leadership, from my book, Life Lessons: A Passport for Personal and Professional Success, 2018, I looked at the qualities of successful leadership.

Research suggests that many women appear to be **succeeding** because of **characteristics** originally considered too feminine for effective leadership. They tend to use **interactive leadership** based on:

- Enhancing others' self-worth.

- The belief that the best performance results from satisfaction at work and a higher sense of self-worth.

- Style developed due to women's socialization experiences and career paths.

  From: *Leadership: Enhancing the Lessons of Leadership,* Hughes, Gwinnett, Curphy, 2013, McGraw-Hill

Recently, I interviewed women leaders in my community to determine if their beliefs about the top leadership qualities and their experience matched those of the national statistics that I had discussed in my previous writings. The results matched quite positively to those of national data research, although my study was certainly not scientific. It included women ranging in age from mid-40's to late 70's representing industries of academia, law, government, banking, health care, journalism, and insurance. Their current or former positions ranged from college presidents, attorneys, senior vice presidents, chief operating officers, Emmy award winning TV journalists, hospital administrators and government officials.

Below are my findings based on the questions they were asked:

➢ What are the top qualities of a good leader?

- ○ Integrity/honesty was number one;

- ○ Collaborative, with the ability to build teams and reach consensus;

- ○ Creativity and strategic thinker;

- ○ Good communicator and listener;

- ○ Self-confidence with the ability to speak up with ideas;

- ○ Know and believe in the mission and business of the institution.

➢ Are there differences between men and women leaders?

- ○ Most of the women leaders believe that men are more competitive, and women are more collaborative, and each has been socialized in these styles by society;

- ○ Men believe they deserve the position while women work harder and believe they have earned the position;

- ○ Women need to identify what they want and ask for it;

○ Men are better negotiators for salary than most women are;

○ Men have been better at supporting other men in their careers while women have not been as supportive;

➤ **Do you think that women have had to overcome issues that men did not deal with?**

○ Some mentioned dealing with sexual advances, inuendo and expectations.

○ Becoming comfortable with being the only woman at the table.

○ Not taken seriously as young professionals with ideas overlooked when expressed at meetings, while similar ideas were accepted from men.

○ Received help in "Opening the door" to opportunities.

○ Some offered promotion with pay, but not title.

○ Without Affirmative Action most of the older women would not have had the opportunity to become the leaders they were.

○ Younger leaders experienced less issues with their younger male counterpart, although they received discriminating behavior from older men. This does provide the hope that our younger sisters are experiencing less discrimination as they have entered leadership positions.

➢ **What would you tell younger women who want to become leaders?**

- ○ Plan for your success. Get a mentor and support other women who are interested and have the skills to become leaders.

- ○ Develop self-confidence with a sense of humility; overcome self-doubt. "Fake it until you make it!"

- ○ Know that you "can't have it all." You must decide what you really want. Keep asking, "What makes me happy?"

- ○ Do not be afraid to ask questions and be willing to listen. Seek out those who have the information and ask for help.

- ○ Know the mission and business of the organization and be willing to take opportunities when they appear.

Where do we go from here?

As they used to say, "You've come a long way, baby!" And, yes, we have. But we still have a long way to go! As the women who have gone before us have paved the way, some with giving up families, physical suffering, even beatings and sometimes death to gain equality for us. I believe we have an obligation to them to continue to do what we can to support each other in our quest for equality. We have greater opportunities to develop and use the skills and abilities we have been given and fight discrimination wherever we find it. We must do whatever we can, wherever we can to make the world a better place for all – especially other women!

Thoughts to Ponder:

> What ideas in this chapter most resonated with you?

> Have you experienced any discrimination in your career path, and if so, how did you handle it?

> What opportunities have you had where others helped or mentored you? How can you assist other women to grow in their chosen leadership goals?

Acknowledgment

I'd like to thank the following women leaders who have been role models to so many women and were gracious enough to take time out from their busy schedules to meet with me.

Dr. Sarah Pappas, Past President, State College of Florida and first woman president; Dr. Carol Probstfeld, President, State College of Florida; Deborah Kostroun, former Chief Operating Officer, Manatee Glens and President, Friends of the Venice Library; Christine Jennings, Founder and President, Sarasota Bank and former Chair of the "Sarasota County Democratic Party"; Tracy Pratt, Esq, Attorney private practice; Lisa Krouse, Esq. Executive Vice President, FCCI Insurance; Mary Braxton Joseph, Emmy Award winning television Journalist and Manager of Community Affairs and Editorials for WJLA-TV 7, the ABC Network affiliate in Washington, D.C.; Bettye Andros, former Director of Pathology, University of California, Davis; Shannon Staub, Former Commissioner of Sarasota County and Founding President and Board of the Sarasota Library Foundation.

References

Life Lessons: A passport for personal & professional success, Peg Beck, 2018

www.livescience.com Life's Mysteries, How do Oysters make pearls, Michelle Bryner,

November 20, 2012

Bad Girls throughout history, Ann Shen, Chronicle Books LLC, San Francisco, CA, 2016

www.usatoday.com #MeToo: How much impact has the hashtag made on line, Dalvin Brown, October 13, 2018

www.rockhealth.com The State of Healthcare: Gender diversity, 2016

www.rockhealth.com Women in Healthcare 2017: How does our industry stack up? Halle Tecco, 2017

http://www.aceacps.org/women-presidents/ Women Presidents' Profile, 2017

www.forbes.com Where are all the female college presidents, Josh Moody, July 5, 2018

www.forbes.com/tech/womensmarch 1/23/2017 Crowd estimates data, Jeremy Pressman and Erica Chenoweth

www.pewresearch.org Gender Gap narrowed but little changed in past decade

www.healthcareitnews.com/news Lack of women CEOs is a problem for healthcare, Diana Manos, January 08, 2019

Notes:

ABOUT THE AUTHOR

JUDY L FOLEY

Judy Foley is CEO and founder of Navigate Transformation Inc. a professional services firm specializing in Transformation, Strategy, Leadership and Change Management with expertise in Operations, Supply Chain, Merger and Acquisition. She has consulting and professional service experience working in mid-market companies and private equity in supply chain strategy, executive coaching, mergers and acquisition integration, roles as Senior Program Consultant for supply chain enterprise requirements planning (ERP) systems and processes. Additionally, Judy's consulting focuses on streamlining and aligning legacy Kraft and Cadbury spend systems into harmonized SAP software solutions -spend performance management system (SPM). Judy is proud to be co-founder and a charter member of The Bridge, which is a collaborative organization formed with C-level executives focused on enabling established entrepreneurs to achieve business success.

Judy has held executive positions with multiple high-profile organizations including Checkers Industrial Safety Supply, where she supported the rapid integration of multiple mergers and acquisitions, at Reveal, where she initiated a robust market analysis model resulting in successful sales collateral and marketing campaigns and at CNA Insurance, where Judy led high-impact work teams to deliver a greenfield vendor management organization. She was awarded CNA's Gold Focus Award for significant contributions, cost savings and leadership.

Active in the community, Judy serves on the Norwegian American Hospital Foundation on the Executive Board on Finance Committee and participates in fundraising. Participates on the Advisory Board for The Council of Supply Chain Management Professionals. Past appointments include The Council of Supply Chain Management Professionals as a Board Member and Vice President, The YWCA of Metropolitan Chicago Lake County, IL as Vice President, Executive Board Member and Committee Chair, served on the education committee for Private Directors Association, and DePaul University's Student and Alumni Mentoring Program (ASK).

Judy earned her MBA in Operations and Marketing from DePaul University's Charles H. Kellstadt Graduate School of Business and holds a BS in Business Administration from the University of Wisconsin – Stout. She also completed Lean Six Sigma Green Belt Training at Chicago Deming Association, Six Sigma Master's Program and participated in Leadership America National and International Women's Development Program.

Contact:
Judy Foley
318 Half Day Road, Suite 190, Buffalo Grove, IL 60089
(224) 422-7771
jfoley@navigatetransformation.com
navigatetransformation.com

FIVE

Embracing Change, Transformation and Being Your Authentic Self

Judy Foley

"To be authentic, we must cultivate the courage to be imperfect—and vulnerable. We have to believe that we are fundamentally worthy of love and acceptance, just as we are. I've learned that there is no better way to invite more grace, gratitude and joy into our lives than by mindfully practicing authenticity." —Brené Brown

At different points in our life, change occurs. It could be a change in relationships, family, health, spiritual life, a job or your finances. But how open are we to this change when faced with it? Your ability to embrace the change will ultimately determine your success in managing through this process of on-going change throughout your life. Will the change that you dealing with change who you are for the better, or will the change deviate you from your authentic path in life?

"A common **definition** of "**authenticity**" in **psychology** refers to the attempt to live one's life according to the needs of one's inner being, rather than the demands placed on us by society or during one's early conditioning. ... The call of, and for, **authenticity** - "be thyself!" An **authentic person** is more at peace with themselves and with the world, because they're living the way the want to live, and they don't care what others think." **Anonymous**

I have been in the middle of a lot of change within the last year. My husband and now ex-husband, supported me on this journey. I am happy to call him my best friend.

So, you question what is this journey? I have written a book called RETALIATION at the Highest Level, Why CEO's, Boards of Directors, HR need to Change the Culture and includes my personal story of sex discrimination, harassment and retaliation. It has been an experience that I would hope that anyone who reads this book would not endure. Yet on the other hand it has opened my eyes to a world I was not familiar with.

I will provide you with an abridged version of my experience here for your review. For a more detailed summary of my life and the events that unfolded I would encourage you to read my book. I have had to journey back to this experience in my mind and through my documentation of what occurred to review the facts. Not an easy assignment and many tears were shed. This experience has taken me almost 10 years to heal from. I had a counselor work with me while I was going through this experience and share the psychological aspects that were occurring during the process that I was not able to fully see at the time. The insight gained from this relationship was a key element of healing and allowed me to remain strong and survive the experience. My husband, family and friends support were key to me surviving as well. I also worked with numerous experts in meditation and silence retreats, counselor's, pastor's, trauma expert, energy experts, and reiki experts. In the end a trauma expert and spiritual guide would help me complete the final aspect of the healing.

My trauma expert shared after I had completed the book and the work with her that I would never return to a point of living my authentic life until I had fully integrated this experience into my life. She also shared that we go in and out of authenticity as we remain a work in progress as changes in our life impact us. I had also considered myself as being authentic throughout most of my life - it came natural to me. I even had an FBI agent that was an expert in assessing people state. "You are so authentic, open and honest." Yet I had to think about what my trauma expert had said; I had carried this experience with the burden of only sharing it with a few people. My friends knew I had gone through something terrible but did not know the details. She was right when we keep a secret or silence an experience; we cannot truly be the complete person we are to be. We must walk through it to become the complete person. A culture built on social norms and the powerful people who dictate those terms are often those that want and expect us to keep our experience silent. I was told by a retired HR executive and coach, that I should not share my story or experiences as it as it would impact my future career potential. Interesting, I bought into it. I had really worked hard throughout my life to maintain an excellent reputation and could not believe this had happened to me.

"In order to escape accountability for his crimes, the perpetrator does everything in his power to promote forgetting. Secrecy and silence are the perpetrator's first line of defense. If secrecy fails, the perpetrator attacks the credibility of his victim. If he cannot silence her absolutely he tries to make sure no-one listens. To this end, he marshals an impressive array of arguments, from the most blatant denial to the most sophisticated and elegant rationalization. After every atrocity one can expect to hear the same predictable apologies: it never happened; the victim lies; the victim exaggerates; the victim brought it on herself; and in any case it is time to forget the past and move on. The more powerful the perpetrator, the greater his prerogative to name and define reality, and the more completely his arguments prevail." 1 —Judith Herman*

Below is a brief overview of what I went through:

Have you ever walked into a situation where a person is being belittled or bullied in the workplace? What have you witnessed in the workplace that was uncomfortable, reproachable, or just unacceptable? Have you stepped in, or has fear of losing your job stopped you? Did the workplace also promote a common vision and set of values with the goal of enhancing respect and collaboration in the workplace?

I was a part of an organization that had both aspects above. The company promoted the need for a respectful work culture while tolerating disrespectful and hurtful behavior that undermined the published common vision and values. I loved my job and collaborated well with the people I worked with. I was a top performer and was included in a high-performance mentor program where a senior vice president was assigned to mentor me. I was recognized with the "gold award" for my results and promoted three times at this company. I received a top rating on performance review in February-April 2009. I had experienced growth, development, opportunities, and numerous promotions throughout my career based on my honesty, work ethic, knowledge, and teamwork at other large corporations. When I faced some uncomfortable situations with a particular executive, I set some boundaries in a one-on-one discussion, believing I could continue working with this individual. I never expected the outcome that would come from this discussion and how my world would be turned upside down. Intuitively, I started to see changes that did not feel right. My own leader whom I had come to trust was now retreating from his prior comment to me stating, "You are going nowhere but up from here." I was guided by my integrity and belief that the right thing would occur. However, my new world was one where I was ostracized, excluded, and marginalized my personal and professional respect in an organization where I had dedicated so much of my energy. The legal term was "retaliation," but my life suffered more than I would have ever imagined.

My husband, an executive at a Fortune 500 firm, never believed this would happen at the company he was part of. He stated, "the behavior and tactics shown to me would have resulted in termination had they occurred within his organization, where he worked." Yet one executive I turned to for his insight, shared this occurs in most corporations because they want to protect executives that are key to the organization. He shared this was never about you, it was about protecting the executive. Yet I suffered and felt the long-term effects of these actions taken for almost 10 years while addressing it.

What happened next for me was not about money, restitution, or finding justice. I learned that many who experience humiliation, discrimination, harassment, and retaliation in the workplace have very few places to go even to understand what happened to them. The legal system provides very little help if you simply want to put your life back together. Retaliation can and does lead to profound personal and professional consequences.

I will now share the journey of change and transformation I went through to achieve authenticity again.

During our time on Earth, each of us passes through 4 seasons of our life metaphorically. We are born, we thrive, we decay, and we die, similar to the natural world during the seasons. The seasons play a larger role in life, and observing the seasons our own life cycle can appear clearer.

Summer

- During the summer, the world is at its ultimate. The trees, flowers and plants are in full bloom. Food is available for all the animals and the temperature is wonderful. Sunlight is shown upon us.

- **Summer:** A season for reward, celebration, and fulfillment.

- My summer occurred while I was producing results and being recognized for my accomplishments at this company. I was consistently well regarded by peers and leadership, and my growth opportunities seemed endless.

Autumn

- As autumn approaches, a slight chill enters the air and the changing of the leaves colors to red, orange and yellow occur. The animals begin to prepare for winter by stockpiling food, the bears begin to fatten up for hibernation and migration of the birds occur.

- **Autumn:** A season for preparation, mistakes, and problems.

- In Autumn, I am approached by a leader I have worked closely with in an uncomfortable manner with innuendos trying to spark a sexual engagement. I attempt to address this concern and set context and ground rules with this high level executive in a one-on-one meeting. I conclude it has been resolved, but unknown to me, this conversation is the beginning of what will become a series of deliberate and purposeful actions to reduce my capabilities, job opportunities, discredit me, and create an environment that works to alienate me- yet I've said nothing; I've remained silent. When I bring my concerns forward to my HR team, I'm not supported nor listened to. How could I raise such a concern about an executive like this? It is evident to me that the machine is working against me, and my thoughts and feelings are of little consequence to the firm I worked so hard to make successful. Winter is now approaching with survival becoming increasingly more difficult.

Winter

- Winter comes upon us and world has become more dormant. The trees have lost their leaves, plants are non-existent, and grass is brown. Some animals leave for a warmer climate and the world is cold and not as much life is around.

- **Winter:** A season for survival, hibernation, and planning.

- Upon acknowledgement of my concern now formally within HR, the cold and suffering begin to escalate and increase in frequency. From being ranked as a top performer, my rating is reduced and I'm subjected to a biased 360 performance review. I'm additionally removed from meeting invites critical to the programs I am leading, and continually exposed to demeaning behavior from the cohort of leaders supporting this executive including my direct boss. Adding insult to injury, I was in line for promotion, but once this situation became exposed, the job description for that role was radically changed and awarded to an individual lacking in skills. I was further requested to train that person given the lack of experiences in a number of key areas. The behavior shown to me continued to escalate to a point where I was formally reprimanded for printing a document deemed personal and not work related. Ultimately placed on a performance review, they classified me as met most requirements when legal and I believe we have more than met the requirements, and then unceremoniously fired. Winter had proven to expose a harsh reality – Once you speak up, you're on your own.

- My experience during winter was one of survival and continuing to be the best employee I could be under the pressure I was feeling during sexual discrimination, harassment and retaliation at the company. I needed to be perfect in every way as they were looking for a reason to fire me and easy out for them rather than truly addressing what the problem was and fixing root cause.

- Winter was losing my job when I had worked so hard for the company and achieved so much to benefit the organization.

- *"If we had no winter, the spring would not be so pleasant. If we did not taste adversity then prosperity would not be so welcome."* Anne Bradstreet

Spring

- Spring is the beginning of a brighter life and flourishing flowers and greenery comes back to life. The earth is back and alive after the winter hibernation.

- **Spring:** A season for rising, learning, opportunity and dynamic thinking.

  ○ Time to take action

- After I was let go from the company I worked for, my immediate response was to hold my head high as I knew I had managed through this with a high level of integrity and had spoken the truth during this experience. I met with many executives and managers after I had lost my job and was learning about different careers that I could consider based upon feedback regarding my skills after meeting with them. I was not really ready to go back to work as my trust in returning to another corporate setting had been severely impacted based on this experience.

- I did return to work and consult in 2011, but I no longer had the same passion I once had. I went back to work to continue to help support my family, but it was no longer the same. A mentor strongly suggested I needed to try consulting. I liked being in charge of my own destiny rather than ever having to go through what I went through. Yet once I felt the work was completed, I was done. I had the opportunity to expand this work activity to additional assignments at the time but chose not to because I no longer enjoyed working as I had previously throughout my career.

- I refocused my efforts and began to volunteer for 3 years to build out my skills through Board of Directors opportunities for the YWCA and professional associations. I was instrumental in creating an organization that helps established entrepreneurs take their business to the next level. This was fun and safe for me. I was using my skills.

- Now I am now ready for the next chapter of my life after coming to closure on this horrific experience by writing my book. I am planning on people opening doors and not closing them based on this experience. I would like to use this experience to help other companies change their culture and outcomes. I also would like to work with victims to overcome their experience. I am dreaming again.

- *"I don't want to get to the end of my life and find that I lived just the length of it. I want to have lived the width of it as well."*
Diane Ackerman

On my journey of healing, I have been exposed to very powerful leaders and professionals who have shared personal stories of their trials in their career or personal life. These people showed me other expertise or skills that I did not see in myself. It was a gift to me to meet these people, hear their stories, and see my skill sets from others' views and expertise. I appreciated their stories, as they made me realize that they too had had experiences that were not what they expected – and learned from them.

I also met other individuals with different outlooks. Some were all about themselves, their accomplishments, and doing whatever it took to get ahead. Some were men and women who cheated on their spouses and chased temporary happiness. But I've also met very accomplished people who are making a difference in the world, not just for themselves but for others. I have seen those who need to find their way on their own path. Others have given up on their dreams. Yet I believe we all make a difference in the world through our experiences.

What I know from all of this is that no one's life is perfect, and when someone makes it appear so, know there have been obstacles along the way that have helped create who they are. The key is to establish our priorities annually and never lose focus, even when those obstacles appear. We must take accountability for our lives, achieve happiness, follow through on daily appreciation, and never give up on ourselves or the people we love. For me, believing in a higher power was key. I could not have made it without my faith in God and the support of my husband and family!

The Seasons of life is about transformation and change. Every experience helps us grow and develop psychologically which helps us become stronger to overcome obstacles and meet challenges. They are about the process of effectively transitioning from one set of conditions or circumstances to another — enabling us to learn, grow and consequently reap the rewards that life eventually brings our way. Being authentic and being thyself for me now means being open and sharing my experiences so other can learn from it and not allow this to occur for others. My future holds so much promise. All blessings passed my way are appreciated.

Resources:
1-Herman, Judith Lewis. *Trauma and Recovery.* Basic Books, New York, NY 1992.

ABOUT THE AUTHOR

DR. SUZANNE MARLOWE MINARCINE

Dr. Suzanne Marlowe Minarcine is a wife, mother, grandmother, community leader, musician, nurse, retired airline pilot, strategist, artist, and founding partner of Sky High Aerial Drones, an aerial photography and aviation education company. Dr. Minarcine is the President and CEO of the Organization for Research and Community Development Global, a non-profit which grew out of Afghanistan and currently serves 22 countries.

Suzanne is an active writer, speaker, coach, and trainer. She is a seasoned entrepreneur who has successfully established and operated four businesses, including an adult day care center, a hospice, a flight school with 89 aircraft, and a home care company. She has a couple of new projects in the works, so stay tuned!

Suzanne believes in living life to its fullest and is always looking for the next adventure. She lives in Macon, Georgia, with her husband, Robert, and her cat, Chanel. Her three children and nine grandchildren frequently pop in and out.

SIX

Becoming Me, Becoming You

Dr. Suzanne Minarcine

I was 13 years old when I knew, without a shadow of a doubt, that I was leaving Payne Road and Thomasville and everything that went along with it. I know when the idea bubbled up into my consciousness, too. I was pulling tobacco. Imagine this: long, straight, narrow rows, just wide enough for the mule to pull the sled. Not wide enough for the tractor. A hot summer day. I was the only girl. I'm not sure why PawPaw let me go out there and do that, but I always played with the boys anyway. It was backbreaking work, because the kind of tobacco PawPaw grew had to be pulled from the bottom up, three leaves at a time. "Asses and elbows," he would call from the other side of the field. He probably didn't want me to hear that, but I did. Regardless, my identity was not going to be tied to the farm.

I didn't know how I was going to do it, but I knew I was going somewhere far away from Payne Road. I loved the legacy of the family land and the road named after my ancestors, but I was getting out.

Somehow, I would do it, and I knew it would take education and hard work. I wasn't ever afraid of hard work, because I learned that in the tobacco fields.

Since that time, I've somehow been able to be sensitive to that inner voice and have known when it was time to make a change and "move on down the road." Sometimes I've moved to a different city, but sometimes it has just been a new job, or even a different career. Each time, I have had to reinvent myself in a new place or a new job, with new priorities and responsibilities.

None of us are stagnant in our lives. None of us are the same people we were when we were born. We have continued to grow and evolve, and, whether we know it or not, we adapt to our surroundings and we pick up new habits, good or bad. Maybe we change our religion or our political party affiliation, but sometimes, circumstances require us to do a total reboot. I used to think this was a reinvention, but I've since come to realize it is more like shaking up a snow globe or scrambling eggs. The same ingredients are there, but they're just moved around a little. You can't shake away your past. You can change how you are perceived, and you can change your thoughts and habits. But the circumstances of your past are always going to be there. It takes hard work and determination to make a dramatic change.

Have you ever had an identity you just wanted to lose? Have you ever just wanted to be anonymous? Have you ever just wanted people to forget something about you or your life? Have you ever just wanted something different? I certainly have, more than once.

My most dramatic reinvention was in 1997 when I left a lucrative executive position and started a flight school. About this same time, I divorced my husband of 15 years. Talk about disruption, and it wasn't just our family. My mother was furious, and friends didn't understand.

But it was time for me to go, for many reasons. That was a conscious reinvention. I moved to a different community and set forth on a path to get it right.

I knew a woman once, who was the picture of an elegant, refined southern lady. She was highly educated, lived in the right neighborhood and was a member of the right clubs. She was considered a leader in her community. What is so fascinating, at least to me, is how this woman overcame her past. I met her when she was in her late 70s, though she would never admit to her age. At 16, she got pregnant by a much older man. I'm not sure whether they were ever married or not because she never talked of him. In her 30s and 40s, one of her sons committed suicide and another died in a mental hospital. Another of her sons was a drug addict. But this woman was a master at keeping her personal life hidden, except to a very small group of people. Even this group only knew bits and pieces. For many years I thought she had simply moved away from her hometown to another town and reinvented herself. She did build a new life for herself, with new friends and a new home, but she carried the baggage with her. The baggage was neatly packaged and tucked away in the closet of her mind, where no one ever would ever see it. She drew upon the skills she has been forced to develop because of the tragedies she endured, and while the baggage may have been moved and maybe not obviously visible, the heartbreak and the ordeals are still part of the tapestry that makes up the fabric of her life.

Think for a minute back to the time when you were a child. Did you ever have one of those small toy looms to make potholders? I always loved them, and my grandchildren love them today. Give them each a loom and a bag of the stretchy loops and they can be entertained for hours, or until they run out of loops. We have a drawer full of potholders in our kitchen, and every single one of them is precious. You start out with the vertical loops. Shall we use only red ones? Or shall we change it around and use green, blue, red, and white? There isn't only one best way, since sometimes you must make do with what you've got. Then how do we weave the horizontal loops? Do we start over and under, or under and over? What color do we choose? The possibilities are limited only by our imagination and the colors of the loops that come in the bag. But we are forced to make decisions.

Now think about your life. We are born with advantages and disadvantages. We are all born into families with their own rich histories. We do not choose our DNA and we do not choose our families. We don't choose the advantages that come to us at birth, nor do we choose the inherent disadvantages that might come with gender or ethnicity. But we take what we get and we run with it. We make decisions as we grow, and all of these are woven into our lives, just like the potholder. We can move things around and we can make it prettier, but we can't erase our past decisions and we can't erase our DNA. We are stuck with all of that, just like you have one bag of loops.

Think about the worst thing that has happened to you; that's easy for me. I can't erase it and I really don't want to forget it, but I don't want it to be in the forefront of what people remember when they think about me. Yet those bad decisions, tragedies, or painful parts of my life also came with fond memories. I can't undo anything I've done but I can reframe those memories and I can use the lessons learned to live forward. Using the potholder analogy, I can move those ugly loops so they aren't quite as visible. The rough patches, no matter how ugly or tragic, do not have to be the first thing people see when they look at me. More importantly, they did not have to define me.

What kind of mistakes have you made? It isn't even important! It is sometimes far too easy to remind them of other people of their mistakes. My mother's best friend loves to remind me how I was playing hide-and-seek with her daughter, at age 6, and I broke her favorite lamp. It has been over 55 years and I haven't broken a single lamp since, but she's going to talk about it every single time I see her. I've honestly had so many labels that I'd hate to even write them down, and unfortunately, one is "the little girl who broke the lamp." Some of my labels are good, some might border on bad, and some have been tragic. I've been a daughter, a granddaughter, a mother, a grandmother, but I've also been an airline pilot, a teacher, an activist, and many other labels. But underneath it all, I am not defined by a label. I refuse to be a noun of any kind. I am a verb. I am a being who is doing. I'm doing too many things to be confined to a label.

We are bombarded by the negative on social media and on the news, and we may be labeled there by people who don't even know us. Express an opinion that people don't like, and other people come out of the woodwork to criticize you. Social media seems to have given us the right to try and convict people based on limited information, brief statements, or sensationalized information that may or may not be accurate. We jump to conclusions based on what we've read in the newspaper or what we've seen on the 6:00 news, which has only given us the part of the story – the part that is designed to get your attention. We tend to forget that there are human beings on the other side of the story, and that every word that is printed and every word that is spoken on the news is crafted to get your attention. It may or may not be completely accurate, since articles are written so that they attract clicks. The more clicks an article gets means more revenue for the news outlet. The more followers we have, the more popular we are, at least on social medial. This has given us a false sense of reality and has altered our sense of who we are. 1000 friends on Facebook does not mean that we honestly have 1000 friends. It simply means that there are 1000 people who are potential observers of your life. 1000 people who may or may not be there to celebrate your joys. Would these people know you if they passed you on the street? How many of them will come to your aid in the event you need them?

Why am I talking about social media when I'm also talking about reinventing yourself? I have had two family tragedies that blew up on social media. Our granddaughter died in a terrible home accident, and neighbors, the news media, and even people we considered friends took advantage of her death to try and grab their five minutes of fame. Our family was portrayed in the worst possible way and there was no regard for the truth. Facts didn't matter to anyone except our family and were totally ignored. For seven months, the police investigated the family to try and change the accident to a homicide. It was brutal. Rumors circulated and I learned to tell the difference between a "how are you?" from someone who truly cared, and a "how are you?" from someone who wanted me to reveal a nugget of gossip that they could spread to the next person.

Reinventing myself was absolutely essential if I wanted to save my life and my sanity. I had a choice. I could either hide inside our home and be labeled as the grandmother of the little dead girl, or I could take control and hold my head high. Moving away was tempting but it was not an option. I had to come out of the house and change the narrative. I had to take control of my life.

Are you in a position where you need to reinvent yourself, or where you need to get people to view you differently? I have a formula that I have followed, and it has consistently worked for me.

Own Your Story

When you tell your story, it is your story. You reveal the facts that you know to be true, but only the facts that people need to know. You don't run from the truth and you don't run from opportunities to be that fabulous person that you really are. You aren't hiding anything; you are just changing the way information is distributed. When you come out and decide that you own your story and you will reveal what you know to be the truth, other peoples' stories change. They've heard the facts firsthand. They've seen you in all your fabulousness. In that instant, you go from victim to hero.

My daughter owned her story when she went to the State Capital and lobbied for changes. She testified before the State House and Senate, and I cried as I listened to her as her testimony was broadcast live on the radio. Not only did she own her story when she told it, she stepped out and got laws changed to make a difference in other people's lives. She had never talked about the accident before, not even to me. Everything I knew came from other sources and what I could piece together.

Change Your Personal Social Media Policies

When I coach women through personal tragedies or upsets, one of the first things we do is unfriend, unfriend, and unfriend. We change privacy settings so that the entire world doesn't see your pain nor your anger. That friend of a friend of a friend who connected with you, seemingly sympathetic, but you really don't know who they are? Chances are good they are a nosey person looking for a tidbit to share. Your social media friends are not your support system and social media is not the place to air your dirty laundry. Cry all you want, but don't share it on social media, unless you have your privacy locked down and you are close personal friends and can trust every single person who can see what you've written. While I have a lot of friends, there are probably no more than five people with whom I want to share everything.

It shocks me to read Facebook comments on current events. I wonder what kind of hearts these people have that could make them so unkind and judgmental. This brings me to the second part of my social media policy, which is don't read the comments on news articles. I hosted a racial reconciliation conference in a small Georgia town in 2012 which attracted the Ku Klux Klan. The event itself was wonderful, but I was heartbroken by the hatefulness in the responses to the newspaper articles. Stay away from comments – you don't need the negativity.

Step Outside of Your Comfort Zone

There have been times when just leaving the house was stepping outside of my comfort zone, but this is more than just that. Step out into places where you can meet new people and make new friends. Find places where you feel at home. We found our friends at the local community theatre and another community organization. We decided we would volunteer at a few places and get a feel for the culture. We have since made some wonderful friends and eventually I shared our story with a few people, but when I shared it, it was MY story and not the story of the gossips. Other people don't need to know. Let them speculate, if they want.

This has been a good practice for our mental and spiritual growth. In response to the shooting at the synagogue in Pittsburgh, we went to a service at the local Jewish temple. In response to the shootings at the mosque in Minneapolis, we went to the local mosque here in town and took food and flowers. Out of this tragedy came the Women's Interfaith Alliance, which is a group of women that has come together to lovingly explore one another's faiths.

Recognizing Control Issues

I have control issues. I like to plan and organize things and I want things to go according to plan. I usually have a backup plan, just in case. Reinventing myself has never been in any of my initial plans, though I think I have always had a Plan B. Reinventing myself has been the result of a singular event, career or personal, that has forced me to reexamine my priorities and figure out a new direction, and it hasn't always been the result of something unexpected. I reinvented myself when I divorced my husband. I reinvented myself when my job ended. I have reinvented myself each time I've retired, because I've had to find a new normal. What do I do with myself? Admittedly, I am a huge failure at retirement.

If only I had control of everything in my life. I don't. I can't stop what people say and I can't control what they do. My children will ask for advice and then won't follow it. But while I can't control other people, I can certainly control myself. This makes it difficult when I am moving into new places. I have had to learn to navigate around in my new role and to set reasonable boundaries. I have had to learn the ropes and the unspoken rules. You can't control everything.

Cherish Your Friends

Friends are essential to a happy life. They may be new friends, or they may be friends you've had for most of your life. We have a group that meets for lunch on Wednesdays, and these friends keep me grounded and keep me sane. These are the friends you can go out with and see a movie, or who you can call in a pinch. These are the friends who will be honest with you about everything and won't just tell you what you want to hear. These friends are very precious and should be chosen carefully. They have your back. You can trust these friends.

When we moved to Macon, Georgia, I came up with a networking plan. I knew we had to develop a new social circle, but how? We chose things and places we enjoyed, and we started going out. Our goal was to speak to 10 people we did not know each month. It was amazing how quickly we made friends, in a town not known for its inclusiveness.

I met a wonderful lady at physical therapy who wanted to get together a group of women to play games. We both wanted to make new friends, and we used a social media app to find like-minded women who wanted to play card games one day a month. A total of four of us got together for the first meeting. One of the four messaged us after and said she didn't want to be our friend, and she wished us well. The three of us were not surprised, but we were happy to have expanded our circle of friends.

Travel

I'm a huge believer in travel as one way to help you broaden your spirit and clear your mind. My older son, when he was five, told his great-grandmother that she would never learn anything if she just stayed on Payne Road. Now my grandmother thought this was funny, because even at this early age Andy realized that travel was important. My grandmother loved travel but by this time, it was hard for her and my grandfather to go long distances. Travel is good for your mind and your soul, especially if you can spend time off the beaten path. Eat at local restaurants and avoid the touristy places. Be kind, and try to act like a local.

Conclusion

Whether you are changing jobs, moving to a new city, or recovering from a personal tragedy, these are strategies that can help you find your new normal. Life will never be the same as it was before a move, a divorce, a job change, a tragedy, or any other life change, but you control your happiness. You can't erase your past, but you can choose the face that people see. As you shake up that snow globe that is your life, you have the power to change the landscape and store away the baggage the rest of the world does not need to see.

ABOUT THE AUTHOR

ANDREA FOY

Safety, Leadership, Image, and Dreams; are the words Andrea Foy lives by. An International Author and Speaker, John Maxwell Leadership Trainer, Certified Dream Coach and Advanced Beauty Consultant/Ambassador, among her many accomplishments, Andrea has published four books and co-authored 14. A Certified Women's Issues and Diversity Consultant, Andrea specializes in Personal Safety for Women, a PWN Book that has become her keynote for workshops and seminars. She has obtained the rare distinction of Distinguished Toastmaster (DTM) with Toastmasters International and was honored to present on their International stage for her contribution to the Heart of a Toastmaster, the company's first and only book about speaking. She lives in Southern Ohio where her passion is empowering and enriching women to believe bigger and act on their dreams.

EDUCATION:
Bachelor's in Liberal Arts/Communications
Master's in Business and Technology specializing in Management and Leadership.

CERTIFICATIONS:
Women's Issues and Diversity Adv. Cert. - 2018
Marcia Wieder's Dream University, Certified Dream Coach® - 2018
John Maxwell Leadership Certification – 2013

Contact:
www.andreafoy.com (Website)
937.248.4765
info@andreafoy.com

SEVEN

Holistic Personal Safety for Women: Research from the World's Women to Me Too and Safety Tips.

Andrea Foy

Octber 2017, the hashtag phrase #metoo began trending on the Social Media platform, Twitter, led in part by American TV actress, Alyssa Milano of Who's the Boss fame. She revealed her account of sexual harassment and abuse after actress Mira Sorvino and other celebrities began accusing film producer Harvey Weinstein of misconduct. Women worldwide flooded social media with their own painful stories. The phrase "Me too" has been used more than 200,000 times by the end of that October day, and tweeted more than 500,000 times by October 16th. On Facebook, the hashtag was used by more than 4.7 million people in 12 million posts during the first 24 hours. The platform reported that 45% of users in the United States had a friend who had posted using the term. (CBS News, The BBC) hashtag and the movement have since taken down many confessed and alleged perpetrators, powerful men in Hollywood and politics, sports, medicine, music, churches, colleges, and the military.

Milano, who was credited as the creator of the movement, acknowledged Tarana Burke who founded the 'me too' movement in 2006 to help survivors of sexual violence, particularly Black women and girls, and other young women of color from low wealth communities, find pathways to healing. Burke has said she was inspired to use the phrase after being unable to respond to a 13-year-old girl who confided to her that she had been sexually assaulted. Burke said she later wished she had just told the girl, "Me too." (metoomvmt.org)

As of 2019, Sorvino, Milano, and Burke are fighting back by continuing to speak out and encourage others to do so. Sorvino plans to continue lobbying for laws to protect women. Several laws have passed in California since then. Milano continues to use her Twitter platform and other avenues to speak out on behalf of women. Burke is working on a documentary titled *Me Too*. She also continues to speak.

The campaign has prompted survivors from around the world to share their stories and name their perpetrators. Recent reports from the United Nations (UNDESA) and the Centers for Disease Control (CDC) show unsettling statistics.

The World's Women

"Women across the world are subjected to physical, sexual, psychological and economic violence, regardless of their income, age or education. Such abuse can lead to long-term physical, mental and emotional health problems. - The World's Women Report 2015

One of the global issues that women all over the world have in common is safety. Young, old, rich, poor, all races, political affiliations, none of us are exempt. Since 1990, every five years, The World's Women Reports have been created by a division of the United Nations Department of Economic and Social Affairs.

Some key findings of the 2015 report:

- Intimate partner violence accounts for most of the women's experience of violence.

- Prevalence of sexual violence is lower than that of physical abuse; however, in intimate relationships, they are often experienced together.

- Attitudes towards violence are starting to change—in almost all countries where information for more than one year is available, the level of both women's and men's acceptance of violence decreased over time.

- In the 29 countries in Africa and the Middle East where the practice is concentrated, more than 125 million girls and women alive today have been subjected to female genital mutilation.

- In most countries, less than half of the women who experienced violence sought the help of any sort, and among those who did, most looked to family and friends as opposed to the police and health services.

- At least 119 countries have passed laws on domestic violence, 125 have laws on sexual harassment, and 52 have laws on marital rape.

- Availability of data on violence against women has increased significantly in recent years—since 1995 more than 100 countries have conducted at least one survey addressing the issue.

National Domestic Violence Statistics

The Center for Disease Control also keeps stats on women's safety. Some more recent findings:

- 1 in 4 women will experience severe physical violence by an intimate partner in their lifetime. (CDC 2017)

- An estimated 9.7% of women have been stalked by an intimate partner during their lifetime. (CDC, 2017)

- Nearly half of all women in the United States will experience psychological aggression by an intimate partner in their lifetime. (CDC, 2017)

By Race/Ethnicity
- Almost half (47.5%) of American Indian/Alaska Native women, 45.1% of non-Hispanic Black women, 37.3% of non-Hispanic White women, 34.4% of Hispanic women, and 18.3% of Asian-

Pacific Islander women experience contact sexual violence, physical violence, and/or stalking by an intimate partner in their lifetime. (CDC, 2017)

By Sexual Orientation
- 2 in 5 lesbians, 3 in 5 bisexual women, and 1 in 3 heterosexual women will experience rape, physical violence, and/or stalking by an intimate partner in their lifetime. (CDC, 2010)

Human Trafficking
- 24.9 million people are victims of forced labor, which includes forced sexual exploitation. (ILO, 2017) (The International Labour Organization is another UN agency.

In the Still of the Night: Personal Safety for Women

As a former flight attendant, I have traveled extensively alone and learned a great deal about personal safety for women. It has become my passion and my platform. *In the Still of the Night: Personal Safety for Women* was published by Professional Woman Network. I have contributed to several PWN Books about personal safety for women.

For this book, I have created a short quiz on how well you know your safety as well as a refresher. This quiz is to test your knowledge in practical-thought-based personal safety tips, not physical defense strategies. This is about prevention and pro-action not reaction. These tips are to prevent you from having to learn and use defense techniques although those classes can help too.

QUIZ

HOTELS

1) When traveling, which of the following do you do when you enter a Hotel room?

    a) Go into the bathroom and make sure the shower curtain is pulled back and check behind the door.

    b) Open all closet doors and look inside.

    c) Both of the above

    d) None of the above

2) When leaving the hotel, do you?

    a) Get the hotel's business card with the address and put on your person, not in your purse.

    b) Keep your cell on your person, either with a holder on your clothes, in your pocket or a wristlet.

    c) Both of the above

    d) None of the above

3) Your purse gets stolen while you are on vacation or a business trip, do you:

    a) Call your hotel so they can secure your hotel room

    b) Go straight to the front desk.

    c) Go to your room first, lock yourself in and call the front desk

HOME:

4) True/False: Only display your last name on your home's door or mailbox.

5) True/False: Use "We" or a male voice on your answering machine.

6) True/False: Put a wooden dowel or broom handle in the door track if you have a patio door.

TRAVEL:

7) True/False: When away from home, forward calls from your home to your cell phone.

8) True/False: It is ok to check cell phones, social media when in a taxi?

9) What are Gypsy cabs? _____
_____

10) Why is it important to get your own directions and know where you are going before you get in a taxi? _____
_____

11) When driving long distance, why is it important to use only the well-known restaurants, gas stations, and travel areas when you need to take a break? _____

12) True/False: As always if you are followed at night by a car with a flashing light, stay in the car, doors locked, and keep the cell phone ready to use.

13) True/False: When dining alone in a restaurant, it's ok to get up and leave your food or drink unattended and then come back to it.

14) True/False: When someone else book's a hotel for you, it is rude to check the hotel out online to see if it looks safe.

15) If driving alone and you see a car accident, should you stop to help? Yes/No.

ATM:

16) True/False: Try to use ATM machines you are familiar with, and try to use terminals located in banks rather than independent terminals.

17) True/False: Use ATM inside shopping malls that are well lit with much foot traffic.

18) If you see anyone or anything suspicious, you should:

    a)   Cancel your transaction and go to another ATM.

    b)   Hurry up and conduct your business, keeping an eye on the suspicious person.

19) True/False: Never walk away from an ATM with cash still in hand.

CRUISING:

20) True/False: When cruising, it is a good idea to check out your ship's report card before you book your passage.

ANSWERS

1) Which of the following do you do when you enter a **HOTEL** room?

    i)   Both of the above

2) Do you?

   i)   Both of the above

3) While a or b is correct, Go straight to the front desk. Is the best answer, c should not be done under any circumstances.

4) True: Only display your last name on the door or mailbox. Even using a first initial can indicate a single person.

5) True: Use "We" or a male voice on your answering machine. For years I had my brother do my messages, even though we didn't live together. He still said "We are unable to come to the phone and nobody was the wiser.

6) True: A wooden dowel or broom handle works great as a deterrent to opening a patio door.

7) True A: This keeps the phone from ringing in your home and gives you a chance to conduct business or be able to give the impression that you are home anyway.

8) False: It is not ok to check cell phones, social media when in a taxi unless it is to tell someone where you are heading. If you are not paying attention the driver can at best can run up your fare, worst can take you somewhere and harm you, and you don't know where you are.

9) What are Gypsy cabs? Also known as hacks. These are usually unlicensed cabs, most importantly most are uninsured. Stick with the cabs with a known company name. Check and know taxi companies before you travel, especially to bigger cities. Don't be in such a hurry that you jump in any cab that stops.

10) Why do you get your directions and know where you are going before you get in a taxi? See answer for #8.

11) When driving, use only the well-known restaurants, gas stations, and travel areas when you need to take a break. Bad guys are less likely to try and approach or harm you in these areas; there are too many people around to witness.

12) True: As recently as 2013 men have been caught using fake sirens and lights to stop women alone at night. A real police officer will not try to pull you over on a dark road. He will follow you to a lighted, populated area before he insists you stop.

13) False: It's not ok to get up and leave your food or drink unattended and then come back to it. It may be drugged. Especially drinks. It is easy for someone to drop an Ecstasy tablet or other 'date rape' drug into your drink, rendering you unable to protect yourself and vulnerable to someone 'helping' you back to your hotel room.

14) True: Use Google street maps to look around the hotel you are staying at. Check out reviews and ratings as if you booked the hotel yourself. If you get a terrible feeling, try and get your hotel changed before you leave. Good companies should accommodate you on that request. Beware those who don't. Be reasonable, asking for a hotel with inside doors is reasonable. Don't be a diva; be safe.

15) No: Do not stop to help people; if you want to assist someone whose car has broken down, use your cell phone and call the Police. Remain at a safe distance in your car.

16) True: Try to use ATM machines you are familiar with, and try to use terminals located in banks rather than independent terminals.

17) True: Use ATM inside shopping malls that are well lit with much foot traffic.

18) True: If you see anyone or anything suspicious, it is best to cancel your transaction immediately and go to another ATM. Use your own discretion.

19) True: If you are going to count your money, do so at the ATM or better yet, put it in your purse and count it in your locked car.

20) True: Check out your ship's report card on the CDC website *before* you book your passage.

RESULTS

19-20 Correct! Congratulations, you did great!

15-18 Correct! Great, but you might need the book! In The Still of the Night personal Safety for Women. Purchase an autographed copy from Andrea's website, www.andreafoy.com today or purchase from www.pwnbooks.com!

10-14 Correct! Consider Personal Safety for Women keynote for your business, corporation, church, college, etc.

5-9 Correct! Consider a Personal Safety for Women seminar or workshop complete with PowerPoint presentation and handouts.

Final thoughts.

Violence against women **exists in all cultures**, ages, religions, sexual orientations, educational backgrounds and income levels. Whether single, a businesswoman, a military wife, widow, college student, or someone whose husband travels a lot; all women need to learn or be reminded of practical ways to be safe and feel secure when they are alone. Despite all the statistics and continued news of the day, there is little reason to live in fear of crime and violence if you are knowledgeable and careful.

This means we **can** go where we want, do what we want and not be afraid of the bogeyman that can hurt us. Knowing how to protect yourself from danger can and will liberate you from not living your life to the fullest.

Bon Voyage!

Notes:

ABOUT THE AUTHOR

SARA DRURY

Sara Drury is a wife, mama and a magic maker.

After years in the beauty industry, she found a missing link between outer beauty and inner beauty so she began years of research and took her expertise beneath the surface to help women bridge the gap from the inside out.

Now this entrepreneur is the leader in self-image alignment and the ultimate Queen maker. She uses her platform to give visionary business women and entrepreneurs the tools create their own Queendoms so that they can create more impact and income in their business and true fulfillment their lives.

She runs popular group coaching programs online that focus on self-image alignment and transformation, and teaching women how to become the person they need to be to have that life they want to have. She works with her clients to remove the self imposed obstacles, and create an unshakeable mindset all of which lead to more success and overall happiness.

Sara is available for coaching, podcast interviews, seminars, retreats and speaking engagements. To contact her, please visit SaraDrury.com or email her Sara@SaraDrury.com

EIGHT

A New Self-Image: How to Create True Change from the Inside Out

Sara Drury

"Imagination is everything. It's the preview of lives coming attractions"
—Albert Einstein

I want to give you a head injury...
    Well, not exactly, but do I have your attention?
    Did you ever see the movie <u>I Feel Pretty?</u>
    Basically it's about this girl who has low self esteem and is living this kind of mediocre life.
    It's about a woman who struggles with feelings of insecurity and inadequacy on a daily basis. Then she falls off a bike in a cycling

class and hits her head. When she regains consciousness, nothing has changed, she's exactly the same person, but because of her head injury, she suddenly sees herself as beautiful and feels all the confidence in the world. She actually believes she is capable of anything. Because her self-image changes all these amazing things start happening for her JUST because she believes she deserves them!

She becomes fearless, and bold and brave.

And literally NOTHING has changed except who she **believes** herself to be and how she now sees herself.

My goal with this chapter is to give you a head injury of sorts.

Actually my true goal is to just help you see yourself a little more as you really are WITHOUT the head injury.

Before I became the leader in subconscious self-image alignment, I spent 10 years in the beauty industry as a makeup artist, hearing things like:

"I'm sorry that anyone will see how ugly I really am without any makeup on. I'm sure they will be thinking cover up those dark circles, and the double chin and the big nose and all the new wrinkles OMG..."

"I will warn you I have hooded eyes and I HATE them"

"I have this scar on my chin and it's disgusting"

Those are direct quotes from clients I worked with over the years.

I think I actually felt my heart break a little each time I would hear things like this, but the thing I noticed over and over again was that even though I could help people feel good on the outside, they still had all these insecurities and misperceptions and there was this gap in how they actually viewed themselves.

I began to notice how broken and inaccurate MOST women's self-image really is. Even with a full face of makeup and dressed to the 9's they still felt inadequate somehow. And I felt powerless to actually help them make a shift in how they saw themselves on a deeper level.

I also noticed that I struggled with this too, and I had for years. I had allowed myself to be in abusive relationships and spent way too much time not believing in myself, not trusting myself, not believing I was WORTHY of what I wanted, or even had what it takes to follow my dreams or live a beautiful life let alone one that exceeded my wildest dreams.

Who was I?

It seemed to me that everyone around me was smarter, prettier, funnier, skinnier, more interesting….

Chances are, you've felt that too.

It took me YEARs to unravel the lies I had been believing. The lies that had been fed to me as a child and lived on under the surface, in my subconscious self-image. They were buried so deep I almost didn't even know they were there most of the time.

But, honestly I got really sick of it.

I got sick of it for myself and for the amazing women around me who were saying the most awful things about themselves.

I got so damn sick of it, that I dedicated my life finding a way to help close that gap.

I started with myself. I was determined to do whatever it took. I found teachers and hired mentors, I read every personal development book ever written, I cultivated the skills I needed, I studied mindset, personal development, the way the brain works, the laws of the universe, and I *implemented* what I was learning. I kept what worked and I got rid of what didn't. I kept figuring it out one step at a time until I learned **how** to feel differently about myself from the inside out. The side effects were amazing. And after committing to myself 110%

and implementing what I was learning... my life started to change, and the only way I can describe it, is that it became "magical".

Actually, when I finally changed my own self-image, I became a real life version of the movie "I feel pretty".

Really! I wrote a book, I went on a media tour, I trained with one of the top coaches in the world, and the leader in subconscious self-transformation, my online programs just started filling up, and the perfect opportunities just seemed to fall in my lap time and time again.

But what had changed? Nothing on the outside. I didn't get plastic surgery, I didn't suddenly drop 100lbs, I didn't get a random windfall of cash (although I did start making more money) ...

And so I got the training and certifications I needed and I started helping other women overcome these untrue beliefs that keep us trapped and hold us back from being the world changers that we actually are and learning how to tap into our inner magic and become who we are really meant to be in the world.

Friend, you are given the dreams that are on your heart for a reason!!! They are waiting for you to achieve them, but unless you start to change how you view yourself (your self-image) from the inside out, those dreams will stay dreams. But if you are really ready to start creating magic in your own life, then keep reading, because I'm going to teach you my method that is so powerful it will feel like magic...

But first, I want to ask you something:

Have you thought about how your negative self-talk or thoughts spills over into EVERY AREA of your life?

We are often too busy worried about our appearance to take the action we need or want to take to better our lives and the lives around us.

This is not an appearance issue, it's a self- WORTH issue.

You think you can't have what you want now because you're not pretty enough, you're not smart enough, not educated enough, too fat, too old, too young, too quiet, too loud, too unprepared, or under-qualified.

But I am here to tell you that is NOT the truth.

You are only living the life you are currently living because of the stories you have been telling yourself.

That is.

You already have everything inside of you that you need and I want to help you unlock it.

I need you to know the truth: Your self-image, who you believe you are, becomes how you show up in the world.

Your perception is everything.

But here's the good news: it can be changed.

You can change your subconscious self-image learn how to BE the person you know you are capable of and unlock the **magic inside of you just dying to get out.**

It's not a bump on the head, overnight change, it takes time, and it takes daily commitment, consistency, courage, and a willingness to be ok with being uncomfortable, but it is possible to be, do, and have anything and everything you want!

I repeat: Who you believe you are will be how you show up. It determines EVERYTHING in your life.

So the key is, if you can learn how to change your subconscious self-image, you can change your entire life.

It really is that simple. WE make it complicated with our thoughts and emotions, because often we hold conflicting beliefs. "I want it but I'm not sure I deserve it", "maybe someone else deserves it more than me", or "I'm afraid of what other people will think" etc.

When you get stuck in a story about how you can't do something, or why you're not where you want to be, you're literally programming your brain to re-live the same day/life over and over.

You can't have what you want in life or business until you understand that you must become who you need to be to have what you want.

The mindset, the charisma, the powerful presence, the beliefs, the self- talk...your entire life, including your what is going on inside of your business is a reflection YOU.

Sometimes we think it's the strategy, or the something on the outside that's broken, but I'm telling you that's WRONG.

If you're not making the sales you want, or creating the business you want... well, you're not being the type of person who can make those sales.

The thing is, you will always ACT like the kind of person that you THINK you are....

So that means that because you THINK you are a certain kind of person you make unconscious choices not to have what you want.

YES... I'm telling you that you are choosing to not have what you want.

Now, I get that you might think that sounds insane, but follow me here.

Your conscious mind says "YES of course I want the best life has to offer. I want more money, I want a new car, I want to lose weight", whatever it might be for you, but your subconscious self-image is the one who holds the keys to the Queendom and if she's not on board it's NOT GOING TO HAPPEN. Your subconscious mind is making the decisions for you.

So let's back up for just a minute and do a little subconscious mind 101 so you can understand how and why this happens, and then I'll teach you how to change it to get what you want out of business and life.

Your subconscious mind was programed as a child. Between the ages 0-11 or so you are basically ALL subconscious mind absorbing and learning from your parents, teachers, peers, TV etc. You can think of your subconscious mind like a computer downloading all the information around you.

You learn how to think about everything from how the world works from what is going on around you.

Once you've downloaded this information you have an internal "setting" so to speak.

And that becomes how you see the world, what you believe is true for you, how you see yourself, what you believe you are capable of. And all of this makes up your subconscious identity also known as your self-image.

This is what basically controls you. It controls your habits, your thoughts and your daily actions. You don't think about what you're going to do most of the time, you just DO it, and you do it to make sure that your internal setting always stays the same. This is the job of your subconscious mind. To keep the setting the same. It does this because it is trying to keep you safe, and it doesn't fully understand the difference between an actual life threating situation and nerves from **doing** something outside of your comfort zone.

So basically, every day you run your internal settings on autopilot.

But remember, your subconscious mind must be aligned with the conscious mind or you will NEVER be who you are meant to be. Your internal setting won't allow for it. You will hesitate and procrastinate, you will be indecisive and unconsciously sabotage your efforts over and over again. That's why you might make a little progress toward a goal, but then something happens to pull you back to your original setting. Think about it! It happens all the time doesn't it?

But here's the thing, when you can get your subconscious mind on board, you unlock your magic! You will automatically start heading in the right direction and taking actions toward what you want. You'll stop sabotaging yourself, and you'll be able to push past obstacles and fears that may stand in your way.

So let's get you OFF of autopilot and show you how to create magic.

You have a dream or a goal right? We all do! Maybe it's the success of your business or falling in love, or having a family, or being your ideal weight. What is it for you?

I want you to get it in your head. Even if you think it's a "stupid" dream or something you think you could never actually achieve, maybe it's something you dreamed of as a kid that you buried down deep and think is a lost cause. If it was ever in your heart bring it into your mind now.

I can show you HOW to reprogram your subconscious self-image and change your internal setting so that you can actually create that dream!

So how can you get your conscious mind to match your subconscious mind?

I created a reverse engineer process that called The Magic Mirror Method and it's designed to help you tap into and embody the best version of you right NOW. And to learn how to create from that place which results in a life that feels so fun and effortless that is seems like MAGIC!

It starts by asking yourself this very important question:

What self-image does a person have, who has achieved what I want to achieve?

Don't just ask it once. Ask yourself this question every single day.

Once you begin to understand what this person is like you can use my process to become this person.

This is what self-image alignment is.

Below I've broken it out into 6 steps:

STEP 1.) BUILD A MAGICAL AVATAR:

The process starts by building an avatar of sorts. Spend some time actually imagining what this version of you looks like, how she carries herself, what her environment is like. I like to get so detailed even down to how she eats and how often she works out.

Grab a journal and write it all out. What would an ideal day as this version of you look like.

Once you've written out the details of this version of yourself, it's time to choose an anchor.

An anchor is something physical and tangible that represents and helps you connect to this more empowered version of yourself. It's a physical reminder of this version of you.

Some examples of an anchor could be: Putting on a bright red lipstick, a special pair of earrings, a beautiful blazer, a piece of jewelry, a special stone or crystal, it can be anything that makes you feel amazing and reminds you that you are stepping into your highest self, your magical avatar.

STEP 2.) CHANGE YOUR BELIEFS:

What would you believe to be true about yourself and the world around you if you already had what you want? I can almost guarantee that somewhere there is someone who has successfully done what you are hoping to do. Someone who has made the amount of money you want to make, someone who has achieved the dream you have in your heart. So, it IS possible. Do you believe it's actually possible for you? What do you think someone who has achieved something similar to what your dream is beliefs about themselves? What do you think they believed to be true about the world and about themselves? Do your beliefs support your dreams? If not let's re-choose.

STEP 3.) RE-WRITE YOUR STORIES:

What would you tell yourself on a daily basis if you already WERE this version of yourself? What would your internal dialogue be? I highly encourage you to write this down, because until this new story is a new habit you may revert to telling the old story. So write it down and keep it close.

Your stories and self- talk literally create your life. So why not start telling yourself HELPFUL /EMPOWERING stories. Not stories of self- doubt and limitations. You have the power to rewrite them and start telling the NEW stories. Your #1 confidence killer is your inner critic aka self- talk. This is what causes the self- doubt and fear of what other people will think or say about you. So start telling (and living) a new story now. I love to help people, I'm doing a great job, It easy to stay focused, I'm so proud of myself, What do you need to hear? Don't wait for other people to say it... Say it now to yourself! "I deserve everything I want! I am worthy of my hearts desires, it's all possible for me."

STEP 4.) ACTIONS/HABITS:

The definition of a habit is: an acquired mode of behavior that has become nearly or completely involuntary. Your life is created by your habits. And your habits are all brain based. But again they *can* be changed! **Habit's are** outer reflections of what's going on internally, and your self- image determines your habits. Just like with our beliefs we actually learn to create habits because of our early environments, and how we were raised. There is a part of your brain that wants you to continue the habits you've created. That's why often it can be hard to change your habits. It is survival based. It's brain- based. The power here is that once you have a basic understanding of how the brain works when it comes to your habits you can create any change you want.

The three brains:

Reptilian- the oldest part of the brain and houses your subconscious mind.

Mammalian- the feeling part of the brain which houses your emotions.

Cortex- the thinking part of the brain that houses your conscious awareness and gathers information.

When it comes to habits most people try to use the conscious part of the brain (the cortex), but the problem is that habits actually come from the oldest part of the brain (the reptilian brain) and that is the one who is in control here! You may have heard the phrase "neurons that fire together wire together", simply put, the more you do or think something over and over again the more it creates neuro pathways in the brain and eventually this becomes a habit. So to create a new habit, you first have to realize what's happening and then start thinking or doing something new and do it over and over and over and over and over and over…. You get the point, but eventually this will create a new habit.

What's one habit that if you started doing would have a positive impact and/or what is one habit if you stopped doing would have a positive impact?

STEP 5): YOU GOT SKILLS:

Now that you're starting to understand how to create change from the inside out, **we can get into action. So what are some skills might** you need to support your new habits? What behaviors might you need to adopt to help you step into this new version of yourself? For me it was getting trained in powerful coaching methodologies so I could create shifts in my clients. I took classes, and certifications and I studied for hours upon hours. Then I had to use my skills with actual clients. So as it pertains to your goals, what are some skills or you could cultivate to get you closer to your goal. For example: if you goal is to lose weight you may need to start eating healthier foods and exercising. Make a list of some skills or behaviors that you need that will help get you closer to your goals.

STEP 6.) MAGIKAL YOU:

Here's the truth: Other people will believe what you believe about yourself and they will reflect that back to you. You've already created your Magical You AVATAR. Start showing up as this version of you now in all the ways that you can control. Take it one step at a time. You can do this slowly and over time.

Literally start dressing the part: the clothes that you wear represent you.

Ask the question: Does this represent how I want to show up?

Go through your closet. What can you get rid of that no longer fits the image of who you're wanting to become?

Go shopping (yes, I'm telling you to go invest in yourself by shopping for clothes) and purchase something even if it's just one thing to start, that makes you FEEL like a millionaire or whoever the identity of the person you're wanting to become.

The thing is, your outer appearance is never really about what you look like, its only ever been about how you feel about what you look like and how you view yourself internally.

Get a "makeover" learn how to do your makeup, hire a stylist, BECOME the person who has what you want from the inside out.

By now you're probably starting to see how this process could work for you once you apply it.

Ok now here is where it get's really good. How to reprogram your subconscious mind:

Once you have a clear mental picture of this magikal you, you can start to use your powerful mind and imagination to bring this vision to life.

To reprogram your subconscious mind you want work WITH your brain like we talked about above. Your subconscious mind will believe the stories you tell it over and over, with consistent repetition. And then, it will start to come up with creative solutions to help you achieve your goals. Yes, there is also a part of your brain that tries to keep you safe at all costs so if some of the "creative solutions" are a little outside of your comfort zone, your mind may come up with more of those excuses or limiting beliefs like we talked about earlier.

So the key here is to really relax your conscious mind, so that you can talk directly to your subconscious mind remember she hold the keys to your Queendom, and we want to talk directly to her, and in order to do that you must relax!

Right before bed or in the morning right as you're waking up are two times you naturally feel relaxed, stay in this state a little longer and start to imagine your new magical self, your desired life…visualize yourself already having what you want, and just for 5 minutes or so, two or three times a day, *pretend that it's true.*

When you're in a more relaxed state of mind your conscious mind will wander and your subconscious mind will be more receptive to the ideas and dreams you show. Especially if you really get into it, with feeling! See it, hear it, feel it to the depths of your soul as if it's real. The way you do when you get into a really good book or movie!

See yourself living in your dream space, having the business success and living the life you want. Imagine it in great detail, as if it is happening NOW. Feel the freedom, the peace the ease and BE a part of the scene. See yourself as committed and bold and courageous! See yourself as you WANT to be.

You probably already know that your brain actually can't tell the difference between real and imagined.

This is what causes magic to occur. The thing is it's not really magic, it's the power of your subconscious mind! She will get on board with you and actually start to look for ways to help you make your dreams come to life.

Inside of my programs I teach how to do this in even greater detail and even have recordings to help you relax and get your brain in the most receptive state to fast forward this whole process.

This was the secret sauce. This is how you can literally reprogram your subconscious mind.

It might seem fantastical or out there, and yes I like to use magical mystical imagery, but this is how the brain works. There is science that backs this up.

Athletes do this, high achieving and successful entrepreneurs do this. And whether you believe it or not, you are already doing it every single day. When you get wrapped up in the fear or the reasons you "can't". When you play out a scene of how you see it going in your mind, you're imagining your life as it is now and recreating the same thing over and over.

So why not interrupt your auto pilot setting and replace the old and unhelpful beliefs with new ones and use it to your advantage. Re-program your mind, change your internal setting, and create a new reality that you choose on purpose, not default. Make this a NEW habit.

I don't want you to take my word for it! TRY it and prove it to yourself! I want you to live your own version of I feel pretty. I want you to live whatever life YOU CHOOSE! And if you try it, you will literally shock yourself as you see what's possible for you when you tap into your own magik. What do you have to lose? It's better than a head injury...

ABOUT THE AUTHOR

Reshma Chawla

My name is Reshma Chawla, I am Software Engineer by profession. I born in India, currently staying in United States, Writing is my passion. Since my college days I loves to write poems, small article. Emotional Intelligence (EI) and Appreciative inquiry (AI) is my true calling. Writing about EI and AI comes to me very easily.

I love to observe people, what they are expressing and how they are expressing, what is their emotional quotient, what is there emotional requirement. I understand emotions goes deep inside than what we express and as human are emotionally evolved species on earth we have most developed brain wiring , Along with advancement our emotional issue become more critical to deal it but knowledge of EI and AI will definitely help us. I want to help people to understand their emotional void, help them to live better life, working as EQ coach is my dream job. Currently I share my knowledge with my colleagues, friends, and relatives and help them to understand their true callings. I always see what is best in others ignore their shortcoming and this beautiful quality turn out to be my passion and I see myself that I can very comfortably motivate others, boost their confidence, help them to understand their true values, their inspiration and help them to progress in their life. My further study in Appreciative inquiry and my new book about Appreciative inquiry will definitely help others.

I am spiritual person and try to follow some spiritual practices, follow guidance of my spiritual Guru. We need to follow spiritual practice to understand essence of human life. In fact I have started my blog "Working_on_emotional_intellegence" https://eqdownloaded.wordpress.com/

To help people understand emotional intelligence with spiritual knowledge in simple ways.

Contact:
Reshma Chawla
Gmail ID : reshma.chawla0112@gmail.com
Blog:
Working_on_emotional_intellegence https://eqdownloaded.wordpress.com/

NINE

Emotional Intelligence for Emotional Souls

Reshma Chawla

It was Saturday morning and my heart started racing. I felt something going on and within a few minutes my pulse rate increased and felt like it was exploding. We rushed to the doctor, and when all checks were done, she suggested a few exercises, and said it was an anxiety attack. I was more shocked with the diagnosis than symptoms. Anxiety attack and me? We came from the doctor with no medicine but the suggested meditation guidelines. This attack was not physical, it was about crumbling /unprocessed emotions kept hidden for years. Emotions that were not about trauma/tragedy but emotions about going through the day positively while battling to get out of bed and start the day. It was about trying to find that missing piece of a puzzle when everything around you was in perfect symphony. It was not depression but it was depressing. I believe myself as the most outspoken person and always talk about my feelings openly, so this anxiety attack made me go deeper into my emotional roller coaster. I felt emotionally empty for weeks trying to fix the hole. I started looking for answers and researched about emotions and the positive or negative effects on body and mind. I was more determined to get the root cause than solutions and along my path I found gold during my research of emotional intelligence.

Emotional intelligence (EI) is not only expressing emotions intelligently but being *aware* of your emotions. EI is like if you're happy about a particular situation, you are fully aware about emotions of happiness, while in a self-controlled mode about expressing emotions considering your social environments. How many of us were outspoken and regretted it later because we were too happy to think straight about the things which should not have been said or if you are very upset about some situation you are fully aware that you are in bad mood and you need to practice self-control, zip your month, manage your actions, and not let emotional boiler run you and explode into angry situations, I have heard a proverb during my childhood, " Don't make promises when you're too happy or too sad." Well, emotional intelligence will definitely help you to obey it. Daniel Goleman has offered lots of research about emotional intelligence and through his books, I really got insight about emotions, human brain wiring, why I have different emotional responses than my friend for the same situations, and why some women speak thousands of words while just acting passively in certain situations with a smile. Some women are outspoken while some dare not utter a word. As per Daniel Goleman, there are five key points about emotional intelligence: self-awareness, self-management, motivation, social skills and being a master of emotional intelligence. He offers several examples when emotional intelligence helps employee performance and financial gain. I compared my experience and it was so true for my professional and personal life. Like dieticians say, 'first we need to be comfortable in our weight', the same is true for emotional intelligence as it teaches us we need to be comfortable with emotions, and when we are more aware of them, we can manage them successfully.

We play different roles during our lifetime such as daughter, sister, friend, girlfriend, wife, mother, and each relationship has its own emotional dilemma and its own beauty along the way. We welcome many people into our world, and a few stay as beautiful memories, while some leave scars. Either way, we remember how they made us feel. Now I would like to provide a few short stories of women who were faced with emotional challenges and how EI finally impacted their lives once they learned to understand their emotions.

I would like to share the story of **Tina's** childhood because for many women, they learn many emotional habits as children and teenagers. Tina had two very best friends who were her world and she was very possessive of them, She had known them since kindergarten and they were very close, sharing lots of teen experiences together. But her world turned upside down as her friends suddenly stopped talking to her and were ignoring her as if she did not exist, She was not sure what went wrong, and they said they wanted to expand their friendship base and explore new relationships. It was not a big deal for her friends stepping away from their friendship with Tina, but for Tina it was a nightmare. It was emotional turmoil. She followed them for a few days, begging them to be friends again. They refused. She had difficulty in the past mingling with others and she only felt comfortable in class or during lunchtime at school sitting with her two friends. EI social skills would have helped with how to start those small conversation, how to take part in those little uncomfortable meeting, about sharing her points and getting them heard even when her heart is racing

Tina was showing tantrums in a variety of ways when she was going through this phase of emotional turbulence and from her parents' perspective, it was just a teen phase. But for Tina , it was far deeper emotional scar that she would carry for years about not trusting others for long lasting relationships, honesty, loyalty, acceptance of others and their choices, and the stress of welcoming new people into her small world . I wish Tina would have known emotional intelligence at that time, as it would have helped her understand the emotional state of being possessive and then demanding acceptance by her friends when they made their own choices to explore the world and other friendships. Tina's friends could also have been more considerate about Tina instead of just throwing their choices in her face. They needed the EI quality of empathy and compassion while understanding Tina's emotional pain. If we taught our teens to be empathetic about others' emotions, it would help to resolve the problem of bullying. EI helps them to understand how our actions would make others feel.   We can welcome many people into our world but we cannot control their actions nor define their actions. Life is about how you manage emotions, get over negative situations, and take responsibility for your actions.

Back to Tina's story...During her college years, Tina learned a few EI skills i.e. self-awareness, social skills , self-management, and starting conversations with new people but she still felt distressed when she talked to strangers, started fumbling when somebody raised their voice against her, and shut herself off from many people. After college she entered the business arena and was having a hard time understanding office politics, sometimes not understanding she was made to do the work without recognition. She was doing her work with dedication but she could not argue constructively to communicate her views to the supervisor, but could easily talk with her peers. When she enters her supervisor's office, her heart is always pounding and she cannot speak for herself; hence she is denied the promotions which she deserves. As she tried to move up the ladder within the company, her emotional skills were as important as her technology knowledge. Although for Tina it was difficult because of her brain wiring, emotional intelligence could be learned and practiced, if she put her heart and brain into it. After EI lessons, she now feels it is better to lose a battle with fighting than let it go without trying. She never gets upset for too long about anyone or any situation, cannot hold grudges, and is quick to apologize if she loses the emotional touch with others. She can now easily brush off failure, situations which hold her down and start with new hopes, looks for new/fresh opportunities and directions to move ahead, and is easily motivated. She doesn't bother with an emotional dilemma of what others will think about her choices, is free as a bird about her social image while her best friends put so much pressure upon themselves to impress others. She has practiced Emotional Intelligence skills and is now self-aware, has self-control, and social skills. She has grown a lot since the "Little Tina" days when she would cry about her friends for days. She now feels balanced and in control of her emotions.

I would like to introduce **Lavanya**, who is my colleague and a new mommy. She was always up- to- date, punctual, and well- prepared for all meetings until motherhood entered her life. It started with nauseous mornings, missing presentations, and frequent bathroom visits, but she was determined to get through it. During her pregnancy she did her best to keep a fast pace as she was aware of lots of competition. It was constant fight in her mind whether to stay or go home . It was not an easy decision, but she decided to take a break from the office after five months of pregnancy. She delivered her child and came back to office after a year, but Lavanya was not the same. Her hair was unkempt, she lacked her usual charisma, was rarely visible in the office, and hurried home after work each night.

One day Lavanya, another colleague and I gathered in a conference room and were discussing some deals we needed to work on . Lavanya just blasted out at our colleague with anger and aggression. She started shaking after that, as it was typical amygdala response triggered by the release of hormones into the bloodstream, which in turn causes the blood sugar to rise, increases body temperature, and prepares the body for fight or flight. She was losing control on a daily basis. But recently her life has recently taken a beautiful turn and Lavanya shares this: " *I never saw the light at the end of the tunnel and there was a battle raging inside of me each day! Technology was moving fast and I never had time after balancing motherhood with career to learn new work-related skills. I wondered if I was ever going to win this battle of being at war between home, children, career and my health.*"

I was in complete agreement with Lavanya, although things often get smoother when the children grow up, I asked Lavanya to keep a journal of her feelings in the morning, afternoon and evening, and then chart this weekly to watch for a pattern. It was important she list the triggers that set off her anger, frustration, or negative emotions. "I was upset because…..."; " I was overwhelmed because……". And on the upside, "I was surprised because….."; "I was feeling on top of the world because……". Yes, it is important to process all emotions and enter onto the emotional chart. She started exchanging smiles and was more open about emotions which were now not necessarily negative. I also provided an assignment to share how she would feel if these hypothetical scenarios occurred: 1) You are invited to a community event about work/life balance after motherhood. 2) You are named as one of the top 10 best women who have worked for your organization. 3) Your children write a school essay about you being their super-hero. These questions gave Lavanya a new perspective about her life, her career, and motherhood. With EI and inquiry, she was able to begin removing her constant mask of negativity.

Layla just retired as VP of a large consulting firm where her days were filled with getting work done, back- to- back meetings, WAR rooms arguments, hanging out with colleagues in the evening, and receiving a lot of attention for her achievements She had little free time and enjoyed the newbies coming to her for advice; her office had become a 2nd home. Layla was now in her 60s and because she had lived a corporate life, she had learned to juggle marriage, motherhood, office politics, put in extra hours at work, and stand toe to toe with her male colleagues in leadership skills. It was a busy life. Now that she had retired, this came to a screeching halt. She had the time to shop and self-pamper, but the sudden emptiness of a lonely life became apparent to her. She was miserable as a retired woman.

One day Lyla woke up and started crying for no reason. In the past, she was a woman who lived her life her own way and surrounded herself by many people, but now retired, she was lonely and depressed. I was sure I could help her with emotional intelligence and appreciative inquiry; however, EI is not magical stick which makes your loneliness go away; instead, loneliness is state of mind and EI can help *deal* with that state of mind because it makes you more self-aware, have deeper self-control, and mindfulness of your thoughts. EI strategies help you to achieve a new mindset faster and to indulge in positive thoughts before suffocating with negative thoughts. I asked Lyla my favorite appreciative inquiry questions: *What is your legacy for your children and how do you want to be remembered by them? What is your legacy for your community and how do you wish to be remembered? What would you be doing if you were living your dream job?* I began to witness her smiling more after several months of self-reflection upon what she had achieved thus far. I definitely saw a shift as she had added beautiful candles to her room and her garden looked breathtaking and well-tended.

She was not ready with all answers to what I had asked, but definitely said she wanted to be remembered by her children as a strong, ambitious woman who is fighter more than a survivor. She says she wants her kids to look upon her as inspiration and motivation while going through life. Moreover, she said she always wants to follow some spiritual practices, go to meet monks, learn meditation from Dalai Lama's place, learn their lifestyle, come back and teach those practices to women who are at similar stages of life. I was moved by how just a few simple questions could help shift her mind and reflect upon how to nurture herself and build a legacy which will touch others.

We all are beautiful women who come in all shapes and sizes, with lots of roles. We speak with emotions; moreover, our faces speak more than our words. God created us as emotional souls... we cry when happy and we cry when sad... and only women can answer why. Emotions can make you fly and the same emotions can put you inside the dark closet. We are not at the mercy of these emotions when you have EI by your side. Most of the time you have the choice to break those barriers of darkness and let go of that brain-wiring holding you back. Celebrate small wins and learn new skills, build knowledge and don't bother to compare with what others have achieved. Embrace your goals and achievements. As my spiritual guru says, "Don't mix your goals with the purpose of your life and along the way you will find your true calling," This is the same way I found my calling as an emotional intelligence coach.

ABOUT THE AUTHOR

PROF. MERCEDES SUSANA PAGLILLA (LIC-EDSP-MED-PHD)

PhD in Education and Magister in Neuropsychology and Clinical Neurology for medical primary practice, former University Professor (Palermo University-UP-Faculty of Communication) and Languages Teacher at Argentinian School Washington DC is an active counsellor for the youth at her clinical private practice being compelled to pursue her researches and scientific contributions in Global Education and Acculturation *phenomena.*

Psychologist (UCU) - she post graduated in Clinical Psychopedagogy (UBA), specialized in Cognitive Post Rationalist Therapy (UP-ICCAP), Drugs Addiction Social therapy (ASA), Master in New Technologies-ICT-in Education (Funiber-Barcelona). After having volunteered as researcher assistant at several pedagogical projects for low resources students at social vulnerable areas in Buenos Aires, she was awarded a PhD scholarship in Scientific Psychology and worked for the Research Institute of Palermo University addressing such specific topics as: New technologies (ICT), Politic Communication, Corporative Social Responsibility and Public Welfare Campaigns.

Professor Paglilla would like to dedicate this chapter to **FABIO VAZ PITALUGA,** loving husband, caring father and partner in life, who is committed to make his contribution as Ambassador of the Federative Republic of *Brazil* for the Middle East in the years to come.

Contact:
mercedespaglill@hotmail.com

TEN

Sisters from the Sand (The emerging role of women in the Middle East)

Dr. Mercedes Susana Paglilla

The following chapter was inspired by my own experience living in Damascus, Syria for the past 6 months. It includes contributions from female Syrian leaders of NGOs and community centers interviewed on the topic as well as my research on other Arab countries in the region.

When it comes to women's roles and their right to claim for gender equality in different arenas traditionally polarized by men, western world ladies stand tall, debate and even though there is still a long run to go, one might say that all options are on the table, so to speak, because there is a robust agenda on women's issues that comprises to change ancient male oriented paradigms from scratch.

But what about women in the Arab world? While it's a fact that social barriers to women's empowerment are everywhere, they are still sensibly high in the Middle East.

It seems controversial that despite the fact that they do have to work harder than men to reach equal planes, rather to be burdened by these constraints, they still manage to find creative ways to work out their restricted range of development surrounded by cooperative spirit, so called sisterhood.

Mostly in those Middle East countries economically broken, isolated and sanctioned by international conflict of interests, it seems that humanitarian crisis reveals its cruelest face thus, as a result, one comes to realize that women might be struggling to cope not only with a single side of the war, but with many kinds of wars resumed in a main one: identity of self .

Let's point out some dimensions that might help us to understand better the Middle East women's emerging role, milestones and challenges in the near future.

Peace Bridges

Syrian women are lucky if born in a family that the father is not called the god of the family = rab al ousrat (in arabic. When the girl sees the respect between her father and mother, and that her mother can work and share all the family responsibilities with her spouse, and when the father gives to his daughter the self- respect and self- esteem, she can decide by herself and choose what she wants to be in the future, and choose her partner without been stuck with all the society barriers. She can love and choose the right person to spend the rest of her life with for better and worse... having this privileges we can say that Syrian women can really build the society after all the suffering we had during 8 year of war and now with the start of a new war - economical war.

Women in Syria now are present in all sectors side by side with men. In some areas we can see only women are responsible for their family and her parents too as they lost their brothers, husbands, fathers and sons during the war.

She is the doctor, the pharmacist, engineer, lawyer, accountant, farmer and above all a mother.

As women were the first victims during the war, as they were subject to multiple violence, they were obliged to flee their home, displaced internally or outside the country. She suffers but is still surviving and helping others.

Syrian women are still fighting to have their rights to be responsible of her own children, when they are still under 18 year's old. She still fights to give her children the Syrian nationality, when the father is non-Syrian or unknown.

Another issue is that a lot of women have to work to support their family and cannot continue their education.

"You cannot have half a peace. ... There is no way you can actually have anything if half of the population is left out" (Activist quote)

Heritage Puzzle Makers

"Women are bearing the brunt of the war and keeping the country together," Randa Slim, the director of the Middle East Institute's Initiative for Track II Dialogues, told The WorldPost. "They are keeping the narrative of a united Syria alive." With the deepest sense of caring and protection of the underprivileged, motherhood spirit prevails and is used as strategy of coordinating vulnerable villages and refugees areas. For example, women power heads every single house in the SOS orphan children village following average family codes, ceremonies and traditions. Children are intended to be educated without stigmas from their past and given the chances to pursue their studies in a family- like environment.

Community Activists

It is a fact that inside and outside Syria, women have been empowering and leading community activism for years as well as organizing politically. Their role emerges as educators, community leaders, activists, workers, and heads of households. Yet, despite their core contributions to society, they still remain barely represented in the political arena and top executive boards.

New Labour Force Players

Women's activism in the Middle East merits as much attention as never before while the region undergoes significant economic change and struggles to diversify away from hydrocarbons, boosting private sector activity, and challenging the status quo. This fact appears as an opportunity for women's role in the Middle East as new structural societal shift is starting to emerge focused on embracing new economic opportunities.

Skillful drivers

Primarily motivated by economic gains, some countries had lifted their driving ban for women. This fact means that thousands of women will now have the chance to work as drivers, thereby replacing foreign expatriates and cutting down on the daily costs families otherwise incur for employing drivers. While car sales are up, women labor participation will increase as they will eventually be able to be recruited for jobs farther from home.

Talented Female-Led Technology Startups

As a way to uplift women who have become innovators in the biotechnology field, Gulf governments have provided scholarships to study abroad. In addition, in the UAE, for example, the Dubai Health Authority has recently promoted the use of artificial intelligence and robotics in medical centers, which on one hand would cut down time spent on routine procedures such as x-rays and physical checkups and , on the other hand, would provide support to surgeons in the operating rooms. As a matter of fact, it is intended that this shift toward a more digitized health care approach would decrease the interaction between patients and practitioners in the future specially when it comes to address some sensitive cultural issues of women interacting with men in the field.

Police and Military Force Workers

Another interesting fact is that Gulf women are cracking the glass ceiling as some countries have announced decisions allowing women to apply for jobs in air control, the traffic police, and the military as well as to apply as investigators at the public prosecutor's office. These decisions are made in line with Saudi Vision 2030, to increase women's participation in the workforce from 22 to 30 percent.

Big Challenge

When interviewed about their fears about the future , one might think that guardianship would come out as a main issue in terms of restricting women's role development in the Middle East. Nevertheless, what comes out first as a main concern for themselves and their children is discrimination. Western geopolitical and interventionist policies against many countries of the region seems to have not only deepened the wounds of extremely damaged economies but jeopardized their heritage identity. Fake media and misinformation does the rest of the job and spreads fear and controversy where what it reigns is a misunderstanding and a lack of education in inclusion, diversity and multiculturalism about the vulnerable groups and minorities.

Now that you have read this chapter, as an exercise of acknowledge about your level of multicultural sense related to the female's role in the Middle East, it would be a good idea to list below some phrases that may define better this role under your perception and so decide placing a "×" in the table case provided whether it might be a preconception of yours or a glimmer of hope.

WOMEN'S ROLE IN THE MIDDLE EAST		
My perception of the facts	Preconception	Glimmer of hope

Now, In order to illustrate this chapter from the own view of a valuable source, I would like to share a letter written by a Syrian friend of mine during an occasion of a social visit intended to focus on a cooperative charity plan to assist some of the most damaged areas by the Syrian crisis.

"… This Sunday 31st of March, we headed a visit on the invitation of Mrs. Hala Barazi, wife of the Governor of Homs, to visit a few institutions for disabled children, and work providing for women whether working from their homes or in factories to support their families.

On the way, it was very saddening to witness from the car windows the heavily demolished buildings. The majority of the city of Homs looked like a phantom city.

After a quick coffee at Mrs. Hala's house, we headed to a school for mentally handicapped children. To see all those children, however disabled but gifted with inner peace and higher sensibility than healthy children, brought me happiness. Their faces had a shining smile that meant the world to me and they had so much more to offer us than what we had to give them. The teachers and educators were committed and very involved in their guiding role. I experienced the same feelings with the latter visits.

Second step was the visit of the Lamsa workshop, crochet, canvas and handicrafts made by women working from home. We were offered a delicious breakfast by 1 p.m. in situ in the banquet room with specialties from Homs like the herrak asbao. Diplayed were items of their fine works to sell, which we were happy to buy. Their generosity went even further as they graciously offered us some soaps and decorative items.

Then we went to a UNHCR local equipped with an indoor playing ground for children. They were playing joyfully with music surrounding. Others were taught to rely on themselves and squeeze an orange to get the juice and draw forms with sand in a container. A young girl told us a nice poem about mothers. We were offered pots with flower arrangements. Kids were smart and eager to make progress in their acquisition of speech, gestures and communication.

Following step was of Khalid Ibn Al Walid Mosque with his shrine, resting alongside his sons'. Afterwards, we went to the Jesuit Brothers convent. In the church, we were greeted with a chorale of young singers led by a female chef d'orchestre performing Ode to Joy by Beethoven. In the courtyard, was the tomb of Father Frantz coldly assassinated with a bullet in the head, with an epitaph in Arabic. Preparations were underway for one thousand persons expected to attend a ceremonial mass on the occasion of five years of his death. Father Majdi insisted on showing us the underground capella.

Al Karim Association for clothes and shoes factory set by UNDP provided work and sewing machines for widows of war, giving them means to feed their children and care for them. Last was the visit of Samedoun Raghma Al Jirah, the Yasmina al Sham Center for Physiotherapy and Reintegration in active life. A courageous team of widowed wives and/ or mothers of martyrs of war, made it a duty to go and visit families faced with tragedies such as heavily injured people, comforting them and taking care of their needs. Such an act of solidarity is totally unseen. Heartbroken and wounded themselves, they still find the courage to help others, and they are mending hearts at the same time as physical injuries. We were shown a video about the nature of therapy and their fields of help. Dentists offer their services in a clinic set with dental equipment. Crochet items were displayed to sell.

We stepped into Julia Restaurant shortly after 5 p.m., Mrs. Barazi extending her hospitality to a tasty oriental lunch in a beautiful surrounding. We could even watch a bride and her husband take pictures on the upper floor. The underground bar was amazing, carved in old stone with antique pillars adorned with crosses and carvings. To top the whole day, Mrs. Hala offered each of us a box of the famous halawe bi jibne, a speciality dessert from Homs.

A word that defines it all to me is DIGNITY. DIGNITY through standing still against all odds, DIGNITY through working to earn a living, DIGNITY well- expressed on the face, DIGNITY in the heart. No begging, no tears, no complaints, but instead determination and strength to survive and overcome the fate they were faced with.

Proud to be Syrian !

It was an astonishing trip !!! And a great lesson of life and hope in a brighter future.

L. C.

Summarizing, when we address the emerging role of women in the Middle East we should contextualize it throughout a mainly male dominated society with a deep sense of religiosity, heritage and family traditions. Thus, while the work ahead for women of the region remains substantial, they have already sharpened their skills to find every single chance possible to work creatively as bread winners or to help their communities within tightly constrained systems. As more economic freedom is introduced to the region and so more opportunities, western women might probably be amazed at what emerges from our sisters from the sand as an outcome of commitment, sacrifice and will of protecting their heritage.

Notes:

ABOUT THE AUTHOR

JANET CHRISTENSEN

Janet Christensen is widely respected as the Transformation Maven! Janet works with clients to create shifts that transform lives and careers. Since leaving her corporate position to start her own business in 2001, Janet has worked with a diverse range of clients including corporate, entrepreneurial, and private individuals. She is a sought after speaker, facilitator, coach, and published author, and has worked with thousands of people and organizations globally.

Prior to starting her own business, Janet had over 25 years of success in the corporate world in senior leadership and management, sales, training and personnel. In her last corporate position, Janet lead two business operations from impending closure to viability and high profitability in a matter of months through employee engagement and strategic initiatives. Janet received official recognition for her performance and contribution from The Canadian Diabetes Association, REALTY WORLD-Canada, and Kelly Services.

Janet is a graduate of Western University. She has 5 coaching accreditations and is a Master Passion Map™ Practitioner. Janet was the recipient of 2013 The Professional Woman Network Literary Award. Janet has co-authored several books, among which are <u>Leaders In Pearls</u>, <u>Creating a Blueprint for Inner Change</u>, <u>Breaking Free Overcoming Self-Sabotage</u>, <u>The Coaching Gurus</u>, <u>The Empowered Woman</u>, <u>The Female CEO</u>, <u>The Power of Transformation</u>, <u>The Young Professional Woman</u>.

Janet's passion and commitment is to help people embrace their authenticity, be empowered, and live the life of their dreams.

Contact:
e-mail: janet@berealsuccess.com
web site: www.berealsuccess.com
phone: 519-868-2262
97 Devonshire Ave., London, Ontario N6C 2H6 Canada

ELEVEN

Being First

Janet Christensen

Busy, busy, busy as a bee…
        When someone asks you how you are, do you ever respond by saying 'busy', 'overwhelmed' or 'I need to clone myself!'? If so, is this a typical way in which you would describe your life? Are you always on the go busy *doing* things - like a hamster running on the wheel, yet getting nowhere? Do you feel that something is missing, even though you are *doing* so much?

The good news is that there is an alternative path to an empowering, joyful and fulfilling way to live one's life by *being* first and *doing* what aligns with who and how you want to *be*.

About 16 years ago I was at the hair stylist's getting my hair cut when seemingly out of nowhere I had an 'aha' moment. I realized that I was a busy person doing what I thought I *should* be doing – fulfilling the expectations of myself and of others, trying to validate my worth through accomplishments, proving myself, doing things in order to feel and be liked and needed. I was on my own hamster wheel, going like crazy, yet something was missing.

The previous year I had left a corporate senior management position to start my own business. However, 'just in case', I was splitting my time between getting my business off the ground and working with my husband in his business. It was like having one foot on the dock and the other foot in the boat. I was busy, going nowhere, getting frustrated and it was not sustainable personally, professionally or from a relationship standpoint. I realized that I was very busy *doing*, yet I was not *being* who and how I wanted to be. However, when I took the time and effort to gain clarity about who and how I wanted to *be* and came from that mindset and energy, I was able to focus and make choices to *do* what aligned with the person I want to *be*. *Being* first and consciously choosing how I invested my time and energy in what I am *doing* enabled me to grow personally and professionally as well. As a result, I was honouring myself and all the other people in my life. I was happier, and I am quite sure I was much nicer to be around.

Why are we so busy *doing*?

It is important to recognize and acknowledge that at a very early age you begin to learn from experience that you are measured, evaluated, valued and judged by what you do, and that this continues throughout life. From early childhood you are acknowledged and celebrated when you learn to crawl, walk, talk, read etc. In school you are measured by grades that you achieve, and you are continually evaluated for your behaviour, all of which gets condensed into report cards and your student records. If you play sports, you are judged based on your performance. When you are an adolescent, teenager or young adult you are asked *'What do you want to be?'*, which relates to a career choice and what you will be doing. It would be very rare to be asked *'Who, or how do you want to be?'*, which relates to the person you are being and how you show up. When you enter the workplace, your performance and productivity are judged and measured and this most likely determines how you are recognized and compensated through salary, performance reviews and career advancement. All this assessing is based on what you are doing and there can be a lot of pressure to perform. The pressure to perform may become equated with your self-worth with the result that *doing* what is expected and achieving success become ends unto themselves.

Life is a journey filled with people, experiences, lessons, challenges, opportunities, joys, disappointments, aha moments and much more. The combination of these life events determines and influences who and how you become and the choices you make. Two people can experience the same event or situation, yet respond and be affected quite differently, depending on their perspective. People are individuals, not clones.

In the same way, each person has unique gifts, talents, strengths, natural abilities and preferences. Obvious examples of this are talented athletes, musicians, inventors, scientists, writers, singers, painters, sculptors, leaders, etc. – those people whose gifts and talents are expressed at a level of excellence that many of us can only admire and even envy. While relatively few people become one of the famous 'natural talents', every person has within them a uniqueness that, when tapped into, allows them to express their true self and live a life of meaning, fulfillment and joy. It is deeply personal. It means different things to and for different people. This is part of the wonder and challenge for both individuals and all humankind in the experience of life as one human race on planet earth.

Much of your teaching, socialization, external and self-evaluations are based on bringing individuals into alignment with cultural norms and societal expectations. You are primarily evaluated and judged by what you do and how well you do it. How do you learn to discover, uncover and express your unique individuality – to *be* first – when there are societal expectations to conform and perform that are based primarily on what you are *doing*? Very little attention is paid to whether what you are doing is meaningful and fulfilling for you as an individual, although when it is, the results from what you are doing are positively impacted. This opinion reflects my life own experiences as well as what I have witnessed with clients in my professional role as a coach and trainer. Real-life speaks up.

When who you are being aligns with what you are doing and achieving, you are in your groove, enjoying being you and feeling good about what you are doing and achieving. *Being first* does not mean sitting on a mountaintop doing nothing in an effort to 'find yourself'. It means being clear and true to yourself, your values, what inspires and is important to you and choosing what you do and how you show up from that focus and perspective.

However, when you are busy meeting expectations and feeling stuck and unfulfilled, it is time to step back, get clarity about who and how you want to *be* and make the shift to come from the *being first* mindset and energy.

"If you are always trying to be normal you will never know how amazing you can be." — Maya Angelou

Being First by Being REAL

You may be thinking that this all sounds great in theory, but after a lifetime of *doing* what is expected in order to fit in, be accepted and achieve, how do you uncover and express who and how you want to *be*? What does it take?

Let's be clear – this shift in approach to life is simple, straightforward and well worth the effort; however, it requires that choices and changes be made and that is not always easy. For some people this may involve some subtle changes and making a few different choices to make the shift. Other people may decide that more substantial changes are in order. Whatever the case, when you are clear about who and how you want to *be*, your path becomes more clear, you can create and follow a plan and trust yourself to choose what aligns with *being first*. It is possible to be energized, inspired, fulfilled and joyful while doing great things. In fact, it is the optimal way to live your life!

Your life is a journey of self-discovery, expression, learning, growing and changing. Embrace your journey as an opportunity to connect with and freely express the unique person you are. Through your experiences you are able to determine your values, connect with your passions, purpose and what you stand for. There is no standing still. Life will continue to give you opportunities to learn, grow and be REAL – Resonant, Empowered, Authentic, Limitless.

Being Resonant

Being *Resonant* involves being attuned to what you create in your life through clear intention, attention, and action. Knowing who you want to be and how you want to live provides a framework to intentionally create your life – your focus, goals, and choices. You create your life through what you intend, where you put your attention and focus, and the actions you take.

Current scientific thinking – quantum physics, chaos theory and non-linear mathematics – validates that we function like magnets and radio transmitters. You are a field of energy vibrating at different frequencies and continually emitting energetic messages. Every thought, feeling and action carries a vibration which attracts other like vibrations. Negative thoughts and energies vibrate at the lowest frequencies. Positive thoughts and energies vibrate at higher frequencies, the highest of these being the vibrations of gratitude and love.

At all times you are attracting based on the vibrations that you radiate, which are determined by where you put your attention. The question is, are you attracting intentionally or by default? When you attract by default you send out a mixture of energy signals, some related to what you want, some related to what you don't want, and you receive what seems like a random mix of desirable and undesirable results. However, nothing is random. What you focus on you create. Having clear intention for what you desire sets up the energy to create it and attracts the opportunities, people and resources to create your reality. You also attract the people, places and situations to help you grow emotionally, spiritually and intellectually. Therefore, look for the gifts in everything that shows up.

Being Empowered

Being *Empowered* is living life on your terms and speaking your truth. The foundation for *being* empowered is taking responsibility for everything in your life. Understand and accept that your choices until now created the results you see today. Taking personal responsibility removes the option of blaming others. While you are not in control of other people, circumstances and events, you completely control your response and attitude toward them. You choose whether to react as a victim or respond with empowerment. Instead of resisting and reacting to the situations and circumstances you face, accept the current reality and consciously choose how you will respond. This allows you to grow and develop through the challenges and experiences in your life. Use your strengths and trust that you will find the people, resources and solutions at the right times to help you move forward.

Taking personal responsibility requires being clear about whose version of your life you are living. Everyone is in relationships of various kinds – family, romantic, friendships, professional, etc. In most relationships, people have expectations of each other and there may be specific agendas. The first step is changing the habit of unconsciously defaulting to others' expectations and agendas by becoming aware of when you are doing this. Look at all of your choices. Do you ever make choices and decisions based on other people's expectations of you, or the need to conform and fit in, instead of on your truth and desires? Recognize when you do this and welcome your awareness; resist the temptation to fault or blame yourself or others. There will be times when you compromise, or do things that are not your optimal choice. Realize that these are also your choices and choose your attitude to follow - will it be resentful or joyful? Relationships are important - choose ones that are mutually respectful and win/win. Understand that your most important relationship is the one you have with yourself.

Where do you want to put your energy? Ask yourself: "When I stand in my power and truth, would this be my choice?" Taking personal responsibility empowers you as you create your life, choice by choice.

Personal Power Vocabulary

Your vocabulary has a significant impact your self-image and how you are perceived. Be aware of the words you are using and shift from disempowering words to powerful words.

Disempowering words	*Powerful words*
I can't (weak/no control)	I won't (choice)
I should (implies no choice/guilt)	I could (more powerful)
It's not my fault (helpless/victim)	I am totally responsible (ownership)
It's a problem (negativity)	It's an opportunity (open to growth)
Life's a struggle	Life's an adventure
I hope (victim/worry)	I know (confidence/power)
If only (whining)	Next time (learn from situation/choice)
What will I do? (whining/helpless)	I know I will handle it

Responding with Empowerment

People commonly react to conflict and issues in 4 ways by choosing to:

- Fight – the best defence is offence

- Flight – removing oneself from the situation instead of facing it

- Freeze – shutting down and not communicating

- Facade – pretending everything is okay. "I'm fine. Nothing is the matter."

Instead of reacting, choose to respond with empowerment to create win/win situations.

Instead of fighting, respond with **courtesy**.

Instead of taking flight, have **integrity** and face the issue.

Instead of freezing, be **open,** communicate and seek to understand.

Instead of putting on a facade, be **honest** about your thoughts and feelings.

<u>All four aspects</u> – courtesy, integrity, openness and honesty – <u>must</u> be present. If the other person does not like what you say, the world will not end. Commit to being empowered and confident by speaking your truth on your terms with courtesy, integrity, openness and honesty.

Being Authentic

"… if you're doing something for someone else's approval, you may as well not do it at all. There is only one reason to do anything: to announce and declare, express and fulfill, become and experience Who You Really Are. Do what you do, therefore, for the sheer joy of it, for sheer joy is who you are. Do what you choose, not what someone else chooses for you."
—Neale Donald Walsch

Being *Authentic* means being genuine and expressing your talents, strengths and uniqueness. If you feel disconnected from your authentic self, the following questions will help you become aware of when you are, or are not, expressing your authenticity. Resist the temptation to self- judge; instead answer as an objective neutral observer would.

Discovering when you feel authentic:
- How am I being and what am I doing when I feel empowered and joyful?

- What are my strengths, gifts and talents?

- What am I grateful for?

- What are five key things that I have learned in life?

- Who are five people that I have positively impacted and how?

- What is my big hairy audacious goal(s)?

- How do I want to be remembered?

Discovering how you self-sabotage and what interferes with your authenticity:
- What are my stories/filters that negatively influence my perception of myself, other people and situations?

- Do I have competing commitments? (eg. balancing career and family; financial obligations keeping me in a job I dislike; my wants vs. expectations of others)

- Do I put others ahead of myself? (pleasing others to be liked; 'shoulds'/obligations etc.)

- What limiting beliefs do I have?

- What fears hold me back?

Use your new insights and awareness to consciously make different choices and express your authenticity. Understand that your ideas and ideals may morph and change as you grow. Ongoing self-awareness is vital.

The following are some suggestions to help you live authentically.

1) Identify your top 5 values. Some common values are: family, health, honesty, spirituality, compassion, peace, courage, humour, joy, growth, self-reliance, truth, independence, education, respect, adventure, responsibility, creativity, balance. Start by brainstorming a list of 20-30 values. Next, prioritize your list to determine your top 5 values. Now clarify what each one means to you in one sentence. For example, you may clarify 'integrity' as 'doing what I say I will do', or 'health' as 'I lovingly care for my body, mind and spirit'.

2) Identify your strengths, gifts and talents. You may ask trusted friends, family and co-workers what they see as your strengths, gifts and talents. A good resource is the book <u>Now, Discover Your Strengths</u> by Marcus Buckingham and Donald O. Clifton. Another resource is the *Inventory of Strengths Survey* on the VIA Institute of Character web site: <u>http://www.viacharacter.org/SURVEYS.aspx</u>.

3) Your *Why, Be, Do*.

    Why are you here? What is your purpose or mission for your life?

    Who do you want to **Be**? What is your vision? What impact do you want to have?

    How are you going to **Do** this? How will you bring your Why and Be to life?

    Express each of these in a concise, easy-to-remember declaration.

For example:

Why: To help create a peaceful and compassionate planet

Be: To inspire authenticity and empowerment

Do: To lead, inspire and create shifts through my writing, speaking and coaching

Your *Why, Be, Do* declarations are a guidepost for your life.

4) Define what success means to you. The dictionary definition of success is: 'Favourable end or result; attainment of wealth or fame; accomplishment.' These are all external measures of success, dependent on something outside of you. While material success can feel wonderful, it is easy to get caught up chasing success rather than paying attention to what really matters to you. When you measure your self-worth and success solely by external measures and conformity, you hand over your power and self-esteem.

The key to authentic success is knowing what fulfills you and then bringing this into your daily life. It is not dependent on what other people do or do not do.

Use the following template to create your definition of success:

I know I am successful by how (quality/quantity) I am (verb) (object of verb).

For example:
I know I am successful by how much inner peace I am feeling in the moment.

I know I am successful by how much joyful abundance I am experiencing in my business.

I know I am successful by how naturally I am being a leader.

Your success statement only needs to be meaningful to you. It is not about the actions or judgements of others, conforming or external results. It is measurable on a personal level – you are either living it or you are not.

Once you have your definition(s) of success, there are two important factors as you implement this. The first is personal development –only you can make this happen. The second is personal evolution - identifying and making the necessary changes to your surrounding environment to support the changes you want to make. Both personal development and personal evolution are required. It is also important to connect with the feeling of your success, visualizing and 'being' this person first, creating the energetic space for it to manifest in your life. When your choices are based on your definition of success you will handle whatever life brings being empowered and authentic.

"If your success is not on your own terms, if it looks good to the world but does not feel good in your heart, then it is not success at all."
—Anna Quindlen

Being Limitless

Being *Limitless* is a natural outcome of being resonant, empowered and authentic. You harness the potential of your body, mind and spirit to tap into what Deepak Chopra calls 'pure potentiality'. If you can dream it, you can do it. History is filled with examples of people doing what was considered impossible and proving naysayers wrong.

While the scope of your life may or may not include history making endeavours, you will create   accomplishments and you will impact the lives of many people directly and indirectly. When you are resonant, empowered and authentic, your impact is positive and inspiring. Opportunities to accomplish great things and to have a positive influence occur daily. Your choices, words and actions impact other people, including strangers who you may never personally meet. You truly have the opportunity to be limitless.

"When you live in alignment with your true self, you send out ripples that uplift the entire universe." —Alan Cohen

What does *being* REAL look like?

Inspiring! Confident! Courageous! Passionate! Curious! Creative! Trustworthy! Amazing! Fabulous! … and the list goes on!

Embrace your journey of self-discovery and *be* the unique person you are. Discover, define and develop the REAL you and every day ask yourself:

"Who and how can I 'be' first and put my whole soul into today?"

Recommended Reading:

Loving What Is by Byron Katie

This Time I Dance! by Tama J. Kieves

The Four Agreements by Don Miguel Ruiz

Infinite Possibilities by Mike Dooley

Notes:

ABOUT THE AUTHOR

SHIRLEY TOLIVER

Shirley Toliver is the Founder and Chief Power Officer at Life On Power. Shirley is Passionate about empowering women and men into believing that they were created the Best version of themselves. Shirley is a dynamic transformational and accomplished speaker, leadership and life coach and has been a leader in Human Resources for nearly 20 years.

Contact:
Email Shirley at shirley@shirleytoliver.com
Connect with Shirley Toliver on social media
Facebook @lifeonpower
Twitter @shirleytoliver
Instagram @shirleyltoliver / @lifeonpower
LinkedIn @Shirley Toliver

TWELVE

Be Full-Filled

Shirley Toliver

People may not remember what you said and what you did but they will always remember how you made them feel. —Maya Angelou

I s negativity consistently drawn to you? Do you frequently experience lost opportunities? Do you have clarity around your purpose?

Fulfillment is the goal for self-actualization and the best strategic plan is the plan that starts at the end; so we start at the end with Fulfillment. Self-Actualization according to American psychologist Abraham Maslow represents growth of an individual toward fulfillment of the highest needs; those for meaning in life in particular. Dr. Maya Angelou's quote represent how individuals who are consistently experiencing fulfillment interact, respond and react in a way that most people who experience them have memorable positive interactions. What you are filled with is how you will Live, Love, Be Relational and Do Business.

There are seven areas whereas we Live, Love, Be Relational and Do Business. It is within these seven areas whereas true Fulfillment is gained. Fulfillment is the key to how we show up and how everyone else experiences us.

Those seven areas are **Spirituality**, **Your Unique Path**, **Relationships**, **Finances**, **Health** and **Wellness**, **Your Energy and Vibration** and **Leadership**.

There is no standard to your **spirituality**. Having one takes the full burden off of you. Your belief system and spirituality will give you Hope and Expectation where you don't see any. It is the foundation for fulfillment.

Your Spirituality is what you will pull from in the most challenging of times and the best of times; it is your leverage. When you can't recognize what you need, your Spirituality begins working on your behalf. Spirituality will influence your perspective in challenging times; taking you from a mindset of lack to a mindset of hopefulness.

It is fluid, it is not religion or being religious. Do not allow traditions, family expectations and "stuff" people say to entrap you into a religious Spirituality that does not work for you, has not worked for you or you no longer recognize. Refrain from living in betrayal and distrust from a previous religious experience, resulting in you choosing to rely on "self". Telling yourself that it's all relevant, and as long as "you do the right thing, the Universe will take care of you is general jargon which is why it doesn't propel you to take action. The Universe needs something to propel it as well.

Your Spirituality is leverage; don't put limits on your leverage. One size does not fit all; it's OK to try a few on for size; you will know which one fits you

Fulfillment Strategies:

➤ Get some clarity about Religion vs. Spirituality

➤ Forgive yourself and forgive others for yourself

➤ Spend time nurturing your Spirituality daily

You have a **Unique Path** and it has a map that contains your passion, your purpose, your plan and your push. This involves you becoming keenly aware of your distinct Passion and the Purpose it serves humanity. Execute the plan to live within your Passion and Purpose, Pursue it relentlessly and vow to push through fear daily.

Your Passion is your distinct natural gift, and no one can do this quite like you. It is usually what you do effortlessly, which is why it is often unrecognized. Once you discover it; your passion will take you from living a good life to living your best life.

Your Purpose is a derivative of your Passion. You have discovered what you do. Why do you do it? This is Purpose applied to your Passion. Before I officially discovered my Power; intrinsically I helped women and men recognize who they are, encouraged them to take a step or leap, and provided resources, tools or suggestions to help them execute. I remember once I had lunch with an executive for business purposes whereas he revealed significant family challenges. At the end of lunch, he exclaimed, "I don't know why I just told you all of my business like that". At the time, neither did I. Now I realize it was my Passion and Purpose colliding.

The Plan will ensure that you actually impact the world with your Passion and Purpose. This is intentional. This is you discovering what resources are needed to impact the world. Will you need to update knowledge through certification or school? Do you need experience?

Do not allow yourself to become overwhelmed with the Plan be courageous enough to ask for support if needed. Just move

Pursue your Passion and Purpose with your Plan relentlessly. Your Distinct Unique Value is needed globally. Do not take your eyes off of the Power. As soon as you succumb to how you impact the world; fear will undoubtedly show up and lead to doubts; and they sound like "you are not qualified", "it's not the right time", "no one will understand", etc. but since living a fulfilled and phenomenal life is not an option you will push through fear as often as needed.

Fulfillment Strategies

➢ Everyone else who is doing it, is not YOU. What are you passionate about?

➢ Invest in your passion and purpose with your time and funds. Don't remain stagnate because "you don't know what you don't know"

➢ Write down three actions items

Your **relationships** are an extension of you. Every relationship deposits into your life. Having clarity where each relationship is within your circle supports healthy deposits and life changing withdrawals.

Every consistent human interaction is a relationship; family, romantic, friendships, co-workers, business partners, etc. We would not experience feelings good and bad without engaging in relationships. There is a strategy for engaging in relationships. It is necessary to determine with clarity where some people fit within our life space. The bull's eye is the smallest circle and designed to only fit a few people. Not everyone belongs in the bull's eye.

Your life space also consists of inner and outer circles. There are people who belong in the inner or outer circles that we have been allowed into your bull's eye; we should arrange people in the order of impact they have on our lives.

Relationships will be emotionally tasking; this is not negotiable. Fulfillment does not equate to never allowing yourself to experience hurt, betrayal or disappointment. On the contrary, when you are living fulfilled you will deeply feel betrayal, hurt and disappointment. With fulfillment you will see the opportunity in the betrayal, invite healing in from the hurt, and have clarity on the part you may have played in the disappointment. Feel the burn, get up, forgive yourself, forgive them and move forward with new tools in your emotional toolbox.

Fulfillment Strategies

> ➤ Who's in your bull's eye? Who should be moved to an inner or outer circle?

> ➤ Love yourself and have a relationship with you first. Finish the sentence; "I Love me because"

> ➤ Forgive him, forgive her, forgive them and forgive YOU. What do you need to forgive someone for? What do you need to forgive you for?

Finances are a means of sustainability and a source of freedom. How you manage your finances is critical to your ability to live within your Passion and Purpose; Inspiring and Empowering others to do the same.

How you manage your finances is emotional, learned and cultural. Every industry has discovered what triggers people to purchase. There is tons of research on how emotions are used as leverage to induce purchasing. Retail therapy within reason is what people who are fulfilled do but out of control retail therapy is how most people react when they are emotionally shopping.

Fulfillment has the habit of creating habits that are worthy of legacy. Your legacy is a compilation of your decisions, actions and experiences including financial decisions.

We learn good and bad money management practices; we can also un-learn and re-learn those same good and bad money management practices. In today's world with an overload of technology; select a learning style that works for you and become emboldened regarding money management strategies.

When talking about fulfillment and finances; cultural values and traditions also impact our financial decisions and priorities. Cultural values are transmitted generationally and generationally if there was a struggle around finances, you will believe that the "financial struggle is real" and will become your normal whereas you will participate in behavior that supports financial struggle. Fulfillment propels you not to accept that you are meant to consistently struggle and instead you will connect with people living outside of the struggle mindset giving you access to tools and resources for a wealth mindset

Fulfillment Strategies

> How are your current financial decisions impacting your legacy?

> How are you serving with your finances? Not just making donations. Look into more purchases from small business owners. See a need and meet the need. Don't shake your

head at the worn-out shoes she has on; buy her a pair of new shoes. There are countless ways to be intentional about serving with Your finances

➤ What do you use your finances for? Take a look at last month's financial statement. How were your finances predominantly used? Needs, wants or legacy?

Your **Physical, Emotional, Mental Health** are essential to your pace of Fulfillment. Physical health lets you empower others to reflect on living in fulfillment. Emotional Health will help you understand your barriers to fulfillment. Mental Health provides clarity of your challenges and will facilitate you loving yourself and others. True fulfillment is living, loving and being relational with no barriers.

There is not one mustard seed of a reason to choose to suffer physically, emotionally and mentally. All the people assigned to you need what you have; your health and wellness is the key to your ability to literally and figuratively give them the hope that they were assigned to you for.

Some of us at some time or another has and will struggle with physical wellness; stopping, starting, stopping and starting again; fulfillment will prompt you to keep trying. Keep trying not only for aesthetic changes, but also for physical health and well-being. If collaterally you lose a few inches and/or pounds, great!

Your emotional and physical well-being are siblings. If you can find 20 minutes to walk around an area in your home daily and listen to an empowering message or music three times daily, you will notice an adjustment in your emotional well-being.

If your mental well-being is deficient, it will most certainly stagnate you and your journey to fulfillment. Life is plenty full of disappointments, hurt, betrayal and experiences that take us to our knees. These are the times whereas the life of fulfillment or the thought of anything remotely joyful seems like just a fleeting thought. Feeling all of life's bruises and bumps and getting back up nevertheless will draw fulfillment forward faster. If you are not healthy mentally though you may need support in this area. Getting help and support is a part of the fulfillment journey.

Fulfillment Strategies
> It is OK to need help and accept help. You have to ask to get to "yes."

> Are you toxic or are the people in your bull's eye toxic?

> What are your top three health and wellness goals? Don't struggle to get to three. If you have just one, get it done.

Everything in the Universe is **energy** including you; your energy will either be a connector or divider. Your personal **vibration** is your Velcro. You will attract and invite in what your vibration is attracting and inviting. Energy goes where energy grows, and fulfillment draws energy for optimal growth.

When you walk into a room, what happens? There should be a shift. That is not to say that you are doing back flips to get everyone's attention. Your presence is the shift. You will feel it immediately, and then your vibration will attract the very person or people who need just a few minutes in your light.

There are a few things you can do initially consciously and consistently that will at some point become unconscious. Make the first 2o minutes of your day count everyday; really be grateful to see another day. This process can begin the night before you retire for bed; read, watch or listen to something inspiring before going to sleep. While we sleep, our minds have a tendency to replay what we put in it before we close our eyes. Become conscious of your thoughts. Your reality is created from your thoughts. It actually matters to look at the glass as half full instead of half empty. The half-full perspective is the fulfillment perspective that again propels further faster expansion and growth. Look for small acts of kindness to practice daily. Instead of becoming annoyed at the person in front of you taking too long with the cashier; read that electronic book on your smart phone that you can't seem to finish.

Fulfillment Strategies

➤ Eliminate Negative Self Talk

➤ Recognize resentment. Untapped resentment leads to anger and spitefulness

➤ Be still. Meditate on something good

The **Leader** practicing fulfillment is serving by sharing knowledge and experiences with other humans who will share what a great leader has contributed to their lives. There's a glitch though; there are no leaders without followers, and it is challenging to lead if you were never a follower. Fulfillment helps you be a good follower to become a great leader. Leaders who are fulfilled inspire behavioral and mindset change, empower actionable steps and generate goals that are specific and achievable for your family and/or your team.

Because leadership is actionable and not a title; the life of fulfillment is never on the mountaintop alone. Choose daily to be authentically genuine, caring, and empowering, while challenging others to achieve results through your actions.

If we are talking about your business, you already have the title on the door. If we are talking about your family, you may have the title on the bank account. BUT there is true fulfillment in shared authority. It empowers those around you and propels them to achieve their goals and it feels safe to fail. You did not become a leader without failing at something.

Being empathetic is what fulfilled leaders do; it is the ability to understand and share feelings of another; it is the hidden power in leadership. It gives you access to expect results and be direct about shortcomings. Authentically fulfilled leaders practice leadership that is quantitatively, qualitatively and are emotionally quotient.

Fulfillment Strategies

➢ Humility is Power

➢ Make it safe to fail

➢ Empathize and expect results

Last week is history, yesterday is the past, and an hour ago is unchanging; now is what you have. Make it count.

Shirley Toliver

Notes:

ABOUT THE AUTHOR

MARLENE PRITCHARD

Marlene is a Wellness Practitioner with a specialty in Anti-Aging. She is certified in Integrative Nutrition and as a Hydration Specialist. As a best-selling author, speaker and blogger, Marlene shares her love on the subject of nutrition and proper pH hydration with her readers along with her personal and corporate clients. She teaches how one may achieve good health and longevity through alkalinity and greatly increase their chances of living a long, healthy, active and medication-free life. Preventative health care is the key to anti-aging and living your best life is Marlene's motto! She has previous publications in multiple anthologies along with her personal book – Alkalinity Matters. Marlene is a wife, mother of three grown children and currently resides in Mississippi with her husband of 32 years.

Contact:
Cell: 601-291-9981
Fax: 601-856-2450
MarlenePritchard@me.com
MarlenePritchard1@gmail.com
KeepOnThriving.com
SangoCoralLife.com
ThriveCorporateWellness.com

Other personal publications -

Alkalinity Matters – A Simple Guide to Being Healthy at Any Age

THIRTEEN

Keep on Thriving An Art of Aging Lifestyle

Marlene Pritchard

It's inevitable… We all are getting older with each passing day. As the days turn into months and the months turn into years, it happens no matter the measures someone takes to prevent this circle of life.

Hello, my name is Marlene Pritchard and it's a pleasure meeting you! Just like most anti-aging enthusiasts, I am always looking to add life to my years by way of looking and feeling the best I possibly can. I'm a wellness practitioner with a specialty in anti-aging.

What I have discovered is creating a lifestyle of simplicity and mindfulness is key. A person needs only to be able to understand the importance of incorporating just a few small changes into their current lifestyle and the results could be both dramatic and life changing!

I'm going to share with you a few key areas that have helped me restore, maintain or even improve my health. I have always been relatively healthy and fortunately inherited good family genes. I am a wife, mother of three, daughter, sister and friend. I have been an entrepreneur and business owner for the majority of my years on this earth. I was in need of increased energy and more hours in the day when I discovered a well-kept secret no one had really shared with me before… so, my story begins…

I was born and raised in the south so naturally I grew up with the southern dos and don'ts drilled into me. Do wear sunscreen. Don't lay out between 10 and 2 to avoid the harshest UV rays of the sun. Eat your veggies. Don't eat after 6 pm for your health's sake. Drink plenty of water. And don't forget to say grace before your meals and prayers before you go to sleep at night. You know, these are the things you probably heard from your own mother that you have passed down to your personal children.

I am very passionate when it comes to anti-aging wellness and was actually practicing this love of mine before I even knew it! I remember going to Dillard's Department store and straight to the Estee Lauder counter to purchase my under eye gel, I would not go a morning or evening without, at the ripe old age of 21! I had no idea this was my initial step into the passion of a world I would grow to love!

I would like to share a quote with you that has been around since the early 1900s. Linus Pauling, a renowned scientist, studied health and the effects made to our bodies by consuming proper vitamins and minerals. As the years have gone by, more and more people have learned of this man and are taking note.

"You can trace every sickness, every disease and every ailment to a mineral deficiency." —Dr. Linus Pauling

What a profound statement! Every time I read this quote, it makes me want to go and grab some minerals to snack on. You see, preventing disease is a great way to keep from aging!

One of the major roles of minerals in maintaining your youthfulness is to keep the proper balance of water in your body. Sodium, chloride and potassium are the lead minerals for this. Strong bones need calcium, magnesium and phosphorous to stay strong and help prevent brittleness. Hair, skin and nails need sulfur to help maintain and stabilize the protein structure in your body.

When you are deciding what foods, nutrients and supplements to put into your body, pay close attention to see if they contain any or all of the following:

Major Mineral List
Calcium, Chloride, Magnesium, Phosphorous, Potassium, Sodium, Sulfur

Trace Mineral List
Chromium, Copper, Fluoride, Iodine, Iron, Manganese, Selenium, Zinc

This list is far from complete but may used as a starting point to help your body become more mineralized. We have many systems within our bodies that thrive when they receive the proper nourishment of minerals. These systems include your skeletal, cardiovascular, muscular, neurovascular, respiratory, and the list goes on!

We all know how we sometimes have difficulty falling asleep and when we do finally go out, we find ourselves waking up before its time to get up. Try taking some extra magnesium to help in this area. All these little mindful decisions one can make take very little effort but can enhance the way we look and feel every waking day! And guess what, getting proper rest helps reduce stress and anxiety so this is also an area that is classified in the anti-aging department.

Are you familiar with the pH of a swimming pool? In order to keep algae from growing, a pool owner must ensure the proper pH is maintained. Our bodies are similar to this analogy.

A healthy circulatory system has a blood pH, which stands for potential hydrogen, of 7.365 to maintain homeostasis. Your body will do whatever it has to do in order to keep this pH measurement in your blood. Your body was perfectly made by God and will do whatever it can to keep this homeostasis.

And here I go again harping on minerals! If you are not providing your body with proper minerals, by way of food or proper hydration, your bones and muscles could pay the price!

We are all born with minerals in our bodies. When our bodies need mineral supplementation to keep our circulatory system in homeostasis (which means healthy!) and we are not supplying it, minerals may be pulled from our bones and joints! Yes, actually taken aware from our own bones and joints!! This could cause your bones to become brittle and fragile. They could become porous and easier to fracture. Not to mention the pain and decreased height people experience when their skeletal system is taking this toll. Postmenopausal women are especially prone to this type of mineral pulling.

I would like to share another quote with you from a Cell Biologist and Nobel Prize Winner that was on the forefront of health and wellness through prevention of all types of diseases, especially cancer.

"The cells of a healthy body are alkaline while the cells of a diseased body are acidic." —Dr. Otto Warburg

There are several ways to have blood tested for alkalinity or acidic measurement. Blood tests are available at one's doctors office but a more economical and faster route is to use pH test strips that are available in stores. These are the same that are used to test the pH in pools. Saliva or urine may be tested and compared to the color-coded chart enclosed in your test kit. Drops are also available to test urine. Again, results are determined by a color match graph.

By now you are probably wondering what types of foods are best and easiest for me to incorporate alkalinity into my lifestyle. I'm all about simplicity when it comes to daily living, so I have compiled a list of foods that could be staples in your kitchen cabinets and refrigerator. By stocking your pantry with alkaline choices, you could easily help yourself make mindful and smart decisions when deciding on your next meal. Believe me, your body will thank you for doing this later!

Try to take notes of how you feel, including energy levels, sleeping more soundly, thinking clearer, etc. before beginning your alkaline lifestyle for comparison later.

Below you will find a list of a few simple but key items you might add to your grocery list.

Alkaline Foods Suggested Grocery List

Major Minerals:
Calcium: yogurt, cheese, milk, salmon, leafy green vegetables
Chloride: salt
Magnesium: Spinach, broccoli, legumes, seeds, whole-wheat bread

Potassium: meat, milk, fruits, vegetables, grains, legumes
Sodium: salt, soy sauce, vegetables

Trace Minerals:
Chromium: meat, poultry, fish, nuts, cheese
Copper: shellfish, nuts, seeds, whole-grain products, beans, prunes
Fluoride: fish, teas
Iodine: Iodized salt, seafood
Iron: red meat, poultry, eggs, fruits, green vegetables, fortified bread
Manganese: nuts, legumes, whole grains, tea
Selenium: Organ meat, seafood, walnuts
Zinc: meat, shellfish, legumes, whole grains

Another easily incorporated major key to anti-aging and living a well balanced and active lifestyle is often overlooked. This is water! Did you know our bodies are comprised of at least 70% water? Water is so important and is so simple but and usually doesn't get the credit it deserves in our anti-aging world.

The brain and heart are each composed of approximately 75% water while our lungs are about 85% water. The skin we love and are trying to take our best care of contains 64% water. Our muscular system is almost 80% along with our kidneys. Our skeletal systems, or bones, even contain about 30% water. Water is the key to life!

"Thousands have lived without love, not one without water."
—W.H. Auden

The cells in our bodies need water to survive along with our circulatory system. Cerebrospinal fluid, ocular, pleural, peritoneal and synovial fluids are all comprised of water. Interstitial cells and lymph nodes require water! *Yes, it's that important! Water is vital for life itself and is required for healthy living!*

Water is vast in our world and can be found all over the world. Bottled water sales have reached an all time high as people are recognizing the need to consume water daily. Baby Boomers wanting to improve the quality of their daily lifestyles are being instructed to drink water to improve how they look and feel. Athletes and coaches know the importance of adequate water intake. People wanting feel better and look better are all learning they can do this by drinking enough proper water every day. It's known as mindful living for a healthy lifestyle!

> *"Pure water is the world's first and foremost medicine."*
> —Slovakian Proverb

I love this Proverb as it is so true! Take care of your body and it will take care of you!

What if you could have highly mineralized and alkaline water? The best of both worlds! Did you know this was even possible? What a simple and mindful way to incorporate healthy living into your daily lifestyle!

Most bottled waters and tap water are known as "dead water." Mineral rich, alkaline water is called "living water" as we experience real hydration at the cellular level when we drink this type of water. A really good website to use as a resource to learn about the drinking water quality in the area you live in is EWG.org. This site will educate you on many aspects of healthy living.

Did you know if your body is holding fluid, such as in your fingers, ankles, puffy eyes, etc., you are probably dehydrated? It's kind of backwards thinking because we feel we have too much water in our bodies but this is not the case. Our bodies will hold water when they do not know when the next "good water" will arrive. The bad part about this is our cells will only hold so much fluid. So what happens to any water you are consuming when you are dehydrated? You're correct! It passes right through you without entering your already "full cells" so hydration to your body does not occur! By the way, this will happen with supplements and nutrients as well. They will pass straight through your body without giving you the nutrition and benefits you are trying to receive.

True hydration will happen at the cellular level when the body recognizes and knows more "good water" will be coming soon. How do we get our cells to begin releasing the water it is holding? This is very simple to answer and has an easy explanation as to why and how we are able get our bodies into a healthy state where our cells will accept and utilize the nutrition and hydration we are providing it.

Alkalinity is key! I go back to this simple but very important fact of life. Alkaline diets and water will help you turn back the clock on the every day wear and tear most of us experience. When a person is drinking highly alkalized water, the brain somehow knows to release the fluid in the cells of the body it has been hanging onto for dear life! One will probably experience urination more often until they become hydrated. Never fear as this is just the body's way of getting rid of extra fluid to make room for better water and nutrition that is provided to it. Is this making sense to you now? It's very simple but so many people are unaware of the effects of true hydration and the healthy effect it can have on how you look and feel each day!

Can you imagine if your joints are really hydrated? Your brain is hydrated? Your blood is flowing freely through your circulatory system? Your muscles have the hydration they need? Is this making total sense to you now? If we take care of our bodies, they will age slower and more gracefully. And isn't this what we are all trying to achieve? Longevity with our families while living a quality lifestyle and enjoying the families and life we have been blessed with!

Although minerals, alkalinity and hydration are the baseline for overall wellness, I would like to touch on a few other aspects of anti-aging and a few practices that should be included with our activities whenever possible.

As we age, we get wisdom. This is a great thing that happens to us all! There are some great brain supplements in the marketplace but nothing will take the place of using your "hydrated" brain! Puzzles, video games on your phone, reading and journaling are great ideas to keep your mind thinking and moving in the right direction. Memory recall is important to stay in tune with. This can be as simple as remembering what you had to eat in the recent past, places you visiting or looking at some old pictures and reminiscing on the experiences and memories.

Joint health – the key is movement! People are sitting too much these days in front of the television. The benefits of keeping your joints hydrated and moving will last a lifetime! Sore and stiff joints are no fun so be sure and keep mindful when it comes to daily movement. Yoga has become extremely popular as it is low impact and stretches the muscles while being easy on the joints. Nothing can take the place of feeling good when you wake up in the morning with little or no pain when your feet hit the floor to begin your day!

As we age, we all begin to see the small tiny lines that I like to refer to as laugh or happy lines. We see our life before us when we look into the mirror. We see experiences and the lines are there to prove it. As much as we love life, most of us want to slow down these creases that begin showing up on our faces around the age of thirty.

Although a happy and fulfilling life is the best medicine, targeted technology brings to us many new and important advances ranging from skincare topicals, injections, various spa-like devices and even light therapy that help us slow down this area of aging. The skin is the largest organ on our bodies and it is vital we take care of it if we want it to always look and feel soft and subtle to the touch. By the way, true hydration is probably the most important and cost effective thing you can do for your skin. Hydrated cells are happy cells not only in your body but also on the outside of your body!

If it always seems that the conversation comes back to water, it does! It's that important! Drinking the proper water, highly mineralized and alkalized, affects a body in more ways than I can list. The circle of life depends on hydration. We, as humans, can go three weeks without food but only two to three days without water!

Being healthy and happy becomes more important to us than ever before with each passing birthday. These two aspects of living have always been at the forefront of the desires in this life and will never go out of style! Do what you can to take care of your body and it will serve you back!

With aging, we either conform and let the body we are born with take its toll or we do everything we can to keep our youth and age gracefully. When we choose to do the latter, we tend to enjoy a better quality of life throughout our living years more so than the first option.

With a few mindful choices and some adjustments in our lifestyles, we may just make the average life expectancy extend to a triple digit!
    Marlene Pritchard, CWMA, INHC, CHS
    Wellness Practitioner – Specialty Anti-Aging

ABOUT THE AUTHOR

Isabelita M. Abele

As President and CEO of the South Jersey-based, family-owned lumber supplier U.S. Lumber, Inc. Isabelita (Lita) Abele has successfully "gone against the grain" and positioned her certified woman and minority-owned lumber and building materials company as a regional leader in industry sales. She represents the best of success in American Diversity as she breaks the barriers of the glass ceiling and opens opportunities for Filipino women and men in America. Her outstanding leadership in a non-traditional woman-owned corporation has been recognized for over twenty-five years with outstanding international, regional, and local business awards and recognition.

Lita spreads her enthusiasm for women empowering women on a regular basis through her participation and membership in women's organizations across the globe, including those that benefit young women. Her motivation to help community extends to her grassroots in teaching and education, where she develops international exchange programs and scholarships for youth entering higher education.

FOURTEEN

Women Empowering Women

Isabelita M. Abele

A female colleague recently asked me, "How many Women's Organizations do you belong to? And where do you find the time to be so interactive with each of them?" I could see it was a surprise to her when I answered, "As many as I can...and I make the time depending on what the other women are like." She had clearly been expecting to hear about some secret formula or a ratio of time vs. effort, but my answer stands. It depends on the women.

You see, if I'm being honest, what makes me join an organization and what makes me choose to stay are two very different things. Not only have my goals changed in recent years, but so have the needs I get from each organization. Choosing one has become less about the trade, industry or potential exposure and more about how we treat each other once we commit to *common* goals.

In my 35 years of entrepreneurship, recognitions and mentoring, the most meaningful part of women who empower other women comes down to how we treat each other as we are working together to achieve said common goals. We may be heading to the same place, but how we walk the path together determines what will bring us success, or otherwise. It has taken me quite some time to come to terms with the idea that just because an organization is comprised of all women, it does not inherently suggest that we are all treated as sisters.

If our collective female voice fails to speak respectfully to and amongst all women, then we remain divided.

Defining All Women, One Voice

I have participated in many groups, associations, and committees that seductively publicize efforts to put forth positive, supporting messages of women empowering women. I have participated in them, I have mentored for some, I have been mentored by others....and I have also *quit*. I say this, not to speak of negativity. Rather to speak of having the choice to seek and find the *right* supporting women who can empower the choices I make for my future. The ones that share my vision, align with my insights and feed my motivations. Women who respect who I am, where I've come from and where I plan on going. Not all female empowerment is created equal.

I recall a time in the not-so-distant past when my participation on an international Board of Directors was a source of great disappointment and setback. I had worked hard to grow my career and my business accolade in order to be invited onto a coveted Board like this; the potential of influence and advancement for my company was right there within reach. Nevertheless, I soon realized that my worth to the organization was defined by my bank account contributions when my first public Board question was, "what is your budget?" Had this female CEO taken the time to discover what other values I could bring to the table, whether by my business experience or my influences in international Higher Education, she would have exhibited supportive leadership rather than the self-serving importance of existing money or power. You see, when women actually empower other women, *together* we realize the money and power that can facilitate change in the world.

It seems I am not the only female business woman to have stumbled onto this observation. *Forbes* contributor Lisa Quast has suggested that women are somehow hardwired from childhood to fight with one another for attention and success.[1] Hers, along with other study results, find that this 'anti-woman' pattern can potentially lead to workplace bullying. In fact, *The Wall Street Journal* quotes that "70% of women are bullied by other women." [2]

*"There is a special place in h*** for women who don't help other women."*
—Madeleine Albright

Given a gender culture where these "Mean Girls" theories may exist, I have become comfortable putting myself first. How? I have stepped down from prestigious appointments, including that of national Board of Director positions. Why? Due to organizational leadership that failed to speak *to* me and *for* me in that unified and magnificent voice we all deserve. Even in all female organizations, we are not united in one voice if our goals and needs do not align. For instance, as mentioned, I have resigned from appointments due to misalignments such as a *primary* focus on making money from members rather than providing a service, or a need for Public Relations to outweigh the resources provided. Self-appointed leaders, selfish administrators, and those who "assign" how I will participate, rather than "invite" my unique skills and knowledge are all Mean Girls I have left behind. None of these concepts were aligned with *my* voice and were therefore not places where I was able to find one voice for all women.

The Change is Upon Us

What does 'Women Empowering Women' look like? As women, we will take responsibility for our own actions toward other women regardless of where they may be in age, career or personal growth. We will;

- Be conscious of the personal ailments, afflictions and pressures we place on one another. They have no place in an empowering community.

- Remember the shoes you've walked in to get to where you are.

- Speak kindly, respectfully and honestly to each woman that crosses your path. They too are walking this journey in the shoes they were given.

- Be humble. There will always be a woman who did it first, did it better or has claimed success for doing it.

- Foster an embracing exchange of differences in culture, origin, status, demographic, etc. A CEO can learn as much from someone else's story as can the student leaving home and heading into college.

- Have a clear plan in place with specific steps for achieving your aspirations in order to keep you focused on your own progress without being worried about what others do, have and want.

- Teach another woman how to create her career development plan.

- Don't judge a book by her cover. We were all sparse details until our stories were written.

- Share your knowledge and don't act like you're the only one who overcame the struggle to learn it the hard way.

- If you have cleared a path, bring someone else along with you. Doing so will not minimize the achievements you yourself have made.

- Make the time. Time is already a commodity; use it wisely to help another woman who has less of it than you do.

- Don't highlight the weaknesses of others with intentions of promoting your own strengths. Success is not a contest – it is a team sport.

- Actively solicit both female and male mentors. The lessons of experience have no gender.

- Have you learned business secrets by working with *men* in male dominated industries? Work on making them Secrets-No-More. In fact, let's stop labeling them "male-dominated-industries" and call them what they are, just "industries".

At the End of the Day...

Ultimately, the concept of women empowering women does not need to come from an organized format of budgeted board meetings and unpaid work after your day job. In fact, you don't need to be a member of something larger to get what you need for your personal or professional growth. If, however, you do choose to surround yourself with the *right* women, that belong to organizational groups or memberships, then do yourself a favor. Do your research, make visiting or volunteering fun, and interview them rather the other way around.

What should you look for in Women's Organizations that have your best interest in mind?

- Those that embrace their members and the value they each bring, not by comparison but by measure of will.

- Those that place a primary goal of furthering the education of its members.

- Those that are drivers of community change by using influence and reach by and amongst its members.

- Those who place importance on the "thank yous" and "pleases", for they will always respect your participation, not just your money.

- Those that offer Mentorship programming that match both mentors and mentees with those having similar goals, but dissimilar backgrounds.

Success doesn't start at the top, it starts at the bottom. To advance beyond the bottom, you must work hard at becoming the leader you wish you had. If you are a leader, you have to be the example you once needed. Sharing goals and expectations with those you choose to align yourself with will ensure that you are not working toward someone else's goal, but instead your own. Consequently, empowering leaders don't just get to the top, they have the opportunity to pull along those who have helped to support them during the journey.

When goals are aligned, empowerment is collective. No woman is left alone when we speak in one magnificently powerful voice for all.

Bibliography/References:

1 Women Helping Other Women? Lisa Quast, Forbes Magazine, 2010. https://www.forbes.com/sites/work-in-progress/2010/11/15/women-helping-other-women-not-so-much-it-seems/#3f7b2a576299

2 When Women Derail Other Women in the Office, Rachel Emma Silverman, The Wall Street Journal, 2009. https://blogs.wsj.com/juggle/2009/01/29/when-women-derail-other-women-in-the-office/

ABOUT THE AUTHOR

Kim Valeri Povey

Kim Valeri Povey, is the Founder and CEO of **Yoga**spirit˚ with affiliated studio locations in Massachusetts and Washington offering programs in Yoga and Ayurveda since 1997. She is the Former CEO of Kerala Ayurveda Academy and brings over 30 years of career experience, as well as expertise in therapeutic mind-body treatments, ayurvedic wellness applications and all aspects of yoga, to her role as a transformation catalyst, mentor and coach. She is a lobbyist and co-chair for the Protection and Access to Complementary and Alternative Health Care for Health Freedom Action in Massachusetts. Kim is a member of the National Ayurveda Medical Association (NAMA) and holds also professional memberships with the International Association of Yoga Therapists (IAYT) and Yoga Alliance (YA). Together with her loving husband Jim they share a blended family of five children. Kim is a musician and competes as an Olympic Recurve Archer. For more www.yogaspiritstudios.com/about-kim

Contact:
(978) 927-0099
valeri@yogaspiritstudios.com

FIFTEEN

Be the Remedy

Kim Valeri Povey

The remedy for wellbeing is through connection. In our global society, we show how much we care through fostering relationships at home, at school, in the office, and through a variety of other social media outlets. We connect and communicate to share stories, offer solutions to life lessons and inspire those we care about along the way. The total woman puts her energy into everything she does with abundant energy, clarity of thought, discerned perception and steadied emotion. She is the glue that binds communities by gathering families and making sure everyone stays in touch. She masters the art of self-care without ever getting depleted. She stays intrinsically connected to the abundant source of love that springs from the depth of her spirit to fuel her lifestyle of wellness. She does not question her equality. She maintains mastery and equilibrium through cooperative relationships with all people and is one with her feminine nature which is as strong and as it is flexible. She has found the remedy for health and happiness lies within her grasp, and the power to control her destiny depends on the empowered choices she makes. From her state of wellbeing flows energy of harmony, goodness, and virtue that become the remedy not only for herself but for her family, her community and the world at large.

The path to becoming a total woman capable of "being the remedy" requires having her physiological needs met, feeling safe, being loved, and knowing she belongs in her world with a sense of purpose. The total woman commits to going through a personal transformation leaving behind all the pain and suffering that once weighed her down. She is free to shine the light she has acquired through knowledge and personal experience. She realizes that harboring negative thoughts and feelings are destructive to herself and everyone around her, so she learns how to assert herself and be heard without raising her voice. She can listen to those she cares for with patience and attentiveness. She does this for herself in meditation, showing compassion and relinquishing attachments to outcomes beyond her control and accepting aversions to those conditions she may need to embrace or oppose. Every woman has the capacity for being the remedy; and can embody inner calm, radiance, contentment, presence, and peace.

We need to be the living remedy by setting the example for those who are struggling to find peace as well as those who are attached to pleasure and power which can be problematic for our society. Without knowledge, wisdom, and structure on how to temper passion for the highest good of our global humanity, our culture will continue to stretch to the point of destruction. The total woman demonstrates her mindfulness, generativity, and higher wisdom as she guides society. She adheres to the principles of her wellbeing and avoids taking careless risks. She has good judgment and higher reasoning. She reflects on how her thoughts, words, and actions affect the whole of humanity and, are therefore, not motivated by selfish actions fueled by greed.

Based on where we live in the world, we may have more or fewer rights and liberties to freedom and opportunities which influence our levels of wellbeing. It is crucial that we are not blind to the experiences others are having or are unaware of the stress factors in our world. In our global family, we call humanity, there is a discrepancy of affluence, leaving some with entitlement while others struggle to get their basic needs met. As we consider what constitutes wellbeing, gender differences can affect our sense of esteem, uniqueness, and empowerment. In a world where connection is essential, we disconnect from our Self and the sacred code of our life. We disconnect from parts of our brain which allow us to be rational and capable of making compassionate, wise and empathetic decisions. We detach from our neighbors, communities, other cultures and countries. We have even gone as far as to be disconnected from nature and the relationship to the planet on which we live.

The remedy is demonstrating expertise at reflecting on one's feelings while self-regulating any adverse effect. It is about remaining in a state of resilience and adopting a strong capacity to accept life's ups and downs using the ability to master real emotional strength while simultaneously mitigating destructive emotional weakness. Being the remedy for my own life came as a flash of insight, in early adulthood at a time when I was experiencing single motherhood and self-reflecting on my life. In that moment of clarity, I fully accepted the responsibility of knowing that the source of lasting security I had been seeking was coming from the deep connection to my inner being. I realized that to navigate and make all the decisions for myself and children, to handle any conflicts that arose, and to be accountable for all my actions was totally up to me. I was responsible for regulating my emotions and reactions and, more importantly, realized I was capable of doing this.

I could not blame without looking at my part in any situation. I did not judge others because I developed an understanding from their perspective and was sensitive to their point of view. I learned that my happiness was up solely up to my ability to cultivate it. I accepted that being alone was not a state of loneliness. I understood that finding mutually rewarding relationships would depend on the choices I made based on who I attracted to my life. I trusted my creativity and founded a school and holistic healing practice to teach, guide and help others. I accepted that I had the necessary skills in the world to provide a sustainable lifestyle and, importantly, found a purposeful life through teaching and healing that offered meaning and value to others beyond myself and my family. I experienced a sense of responsibility to nurture others and contribute to future generations based on the challenging lessons I learned in my twenties.

Healing, Empowerment, and Leadership

It's been over thirty years since the auto accident that changed the course of my life. A drunk driver hit me, and I was taken from my wrecked automobile by the 'jaws of life". I was crossing an intersection at the end of the detour at the top of a hill, and a young drunk driver hit me on the driver's side. My car spun around and around until it wrapped itself around a tree. All the windows were crushed, and the driver side pushed to the passenger side. This accident happened before the era of airbags, and my head hit the windshield while the steering wheel badly smashed my face. I was unconscious for three days and had face, head and body trauma. There was a moment when I accepted what the doctors had told me which was to learn to live with debilitating pain for the rest of my life. I struggled with accepting this fate until I found meditation.

One day in meditation I recall saying "dear God if it is my fate to know this pain for the sake of helping another, then I will accept it. Please give a purpose to my suffering and if it is what you want of me, so be it". In that moment of surrender and acceptance, I found the moments of awareness in between thoughts that offered me complete freedom and pain relief. I used the power of my mind to down-regulate the pain until it was at the level of a mild sensation and then completely disappeared. As I continued meditation regularly, I began the practices of yogasana and pranayama. This stage was a significant turning point in my nine-year journey to health, healing, transformation, and mystical transfiguration. It was transfiguration that moved my body to an optimal state of wellness and health. Due to my tragedy and transformation, I established a mission first through founding Yogaspirit® Studios and Healing Center and later The Yogaspirit® school of Ayurveda to empower others with the tools I had developed and learned. I have inspired many to journey on the path of transformation for the past twenty years.

Emotional Remedies

When we use our discerning intelligence to help navigate a difficult situation gracefully, we can use a mantra or sacred word to help us let go of our heavy burdens. Saying the word, Swaha means "With faith, I give this over to a higher power for the highest good and wellbeing of all concerned." A response like this is very different from saying "I give up, I don't care or it doesn't matter" because Swaha means you are not giving up but rather giving it over. It says you care deeply but can't do it all by yourself. It means that the situation matters profoundly and this is why you offer it up to a faith that guides your every step. A power that is greater than you but connects to the source within you which over time becomes a prominent part of you.

Lesson One: Swaha Mantra in Meditation

Close your eyes, connect with your heart and lovingly let the burden go to a higher power through your intentions to seek help and inner guidance. Watch how this mantra elevates your troubles, making them lighter and lighter until the burden has dissipated into the universal field that supports you. You are no longer stagnant, feeling, stuck, overwhelmed and often depressed or anxious. Your aura of vital energy can freely flow. You will also notice that solutions will come to help you once you consciously place the burden in the universal field. Over time, with patience and practice, the burden seems to get resolved on its own.

Lesson Two: Attachments to Aversions

The fastest way to experience freedom from suffering is to gain the ability to let go of your aversions. If you don't know what they are, try noticing every time you say, "I don't like that, I hate this, I won't do that." Pay closer attention to those things you complain about most or seem to be dissatisfied with and what you often judge. For every attachment to an aversion, there is an equal attachment to something desirable. As a result, you subject yourself to an endless tug of war that takes your energy and whips you to one side and then the other, leaving you emotionally exhausted in the process. The secret is to live in the intersection of these two points, preserving your attention and energy. Liberating yourself of aversions does not mean that you can't take a stand, have an opinion or maintain specific preferences. What freeing yourself of attachments means is that you are not pulled out of balance when things don't go your way. It is beneficial to have more grit, faith, acceptance and the willingness to be uncomfortable at times. Yoga and meditation condition your mind and body to attain this through the actual practice of having focused attention while following steady breath in a physical posture or in sustained seated stillness. Additionally, there are several techniques I use to teach how to let go of aversions. Here is one that helps to neutralize an aversion.

Exercise to neutralize aversions

Contemplate the hidden value in your dislike. Ask yourself, "How is this aversion helping me grow emotionally or spiritually?" Maybe you will learn it is helping you find more compassion, courage, or faith. Perhaps the aversion is helping you to have better boundaries, priorities or make certain necessary decisions. Trust that a benevolent hidden intention is behind the struggle of each aversion and journal about it.

Instead of having aversions, you are no longer *reacting* to your dislikes. They become neutralized and, in this way, you can continue to work at the issues in a resourceful, patient, pragmatic approach. You can accept the process of working through the aversion with more patience, appreciating different points of view, discovering benevolent intentions and gaining a broader sense and perspective of the issue than you could have previously imagined. You become more curious, open-minded, and genuinely interested in the process instead of feeling drained from chasing after an outcome you held emotionally. You become very creative in solving problems, and you are not afraid of engaging in a good debate or learning something you could benefit from understanding better. Most of all you become less toxic, less angry, and less cynical and find it easier to become more approachable, reasonable and resourceful as you assert yourself in a non-threatening way so others can hear what you are trying to communicate.

Physical Remedies

I have numerous remedies for life balance. In this short chapter, I have selected just a few of my favorites to share with you.

Lesson One: Sleep Soundly

Adjust to the circadian rhythm of nature and go to bed by 10 pm. Power down electronics and give your retina and visual cortex thirty minutes to respond to reduced lighting allowing the natural release of melatonin from the brain to promote sleep.

Lesson Two: Eat Organically

There is so much I can say here, but for this one chapter, the point I would like to make is to eat organically as a way to avoid glyphosate found in our food source. This chemical agent is a significant contributor to the root cause of our gut microbiota imbalances, leaky gut, immunity problems, and numerous health challenges.

Lesson Three: Yoga

Find a good teacher who can inspire you to refine your practice, connect the meaning of the poses with the purpose of your life. Yoga should be refreshing, balancing and recalibrating. If you find it competitive, too heated, exhausting or injurious, continue looking until you discover the right teacher and yoga class. Yoga opens energy channels in your body and allows you to have more freedom of breath, freedom of movement, greater vitality, energy, and balance.

Lesson Four: Move Your Body

In addition to yoga, I love bare bow recurve archery, Rose and Rea's Zumba class, going for a walk in the sun, dancing to music and going to the gym with my husband to lift weights – all in moderation. To sweat moderately means you are converting and conducting energy, boosting your immunity, maintaining your life-force, detoxing and contributing to your sense of wellness.

Lesson Five: Adopt a Wellness Mindset

I believe everyone values human life. However, as a culture, I feel there is a bigger problem as our humanity does not have a "preventative wellness mindset"; instead we only have a "reactionary and disease mindset." A majority of people do not understand the nature of the root causes to their underlying health problems. Moreover, even if they are knowledgeable, often they do not have the willpower or motivation to make the necessary lifestyle changes until it is too late. Culturally there needs to be more wellness education and incentive to change the way we look at becoming responsible for our health.

People need to understand how to manage their lifestyle, food, relationships, mind, sleep, and stress. If everyone could learn to self-regulate according to their unique ayurvedic constitutional makeup, we might find that prevention and wellness mean something entirely different than getting checkups. We would be able to recognize the red flags that point to signs of disease before the stages of the condition manifest in the body as disease. Ayurvedic medicine is not one size fits all; there are basic concepts which support approaches to best treatments including yoga, meditation, mantras, and counseling as well as herbal therapies based on one's constitutional orientation. If we stay on the prevention path to health, there would be lower health care costs for patients and well as cost containment for the hospitals who care for them. People become a burden to society when poor lifestyle choices are made over a lifetime. Even if one - had the genetics predisposed with poor health, prevention can transform and beat those odds with strategies employing the science of epigenetics and neuroplasticity which changes mind-body patterns. Due to excellent self-care and empowerment, my mother is remarkably healthy at 80 years old. She has never had to take regular medication. Meanwhile, I was able to turn around my life after a nine-year journey back to health from an auto accident to realize my healing and empowerment with natural methods.

Relationship Remedies

I am a modern woman, but I am also a naturalist and traditionalist. When it comes to identity, my pronouns are she/her. I tend to parallel the macrocosm of nature to the microcosm of gender and maintain a more conventional view of mating and relationships based on how I identify myself. I accept all the ways in which men and women find love for themselves and love for one another and understand the complexities of how society is learning to best express identity and equality. As a total woman, I accept human androgyny and equality in societal roles. I identify with how nature has designed men and women equally yet differently. The polarities of men and women have long been divided creating imbalance and separation. Yoga can unify the pairing of opposites within a person to better maintain equality and harmony.

In a marriage between and man and women:

A couple puts their life and destiny in the hands of each other to provide for their family. A man might put trust in his wife to inspire him with the love and affection that will enable him to have better control over his emotions and reactions to life. Her love gives meaning to how he leads his life, and his love can provide her with a sense of security and trust.

A man might feel insecure and inadequately equipped to regulate his emotions and reactions. He might be looking for security through physical attainment and possessions that give him a sense of power which might lead him to the behavior of dominance and control. However, what about his sense of purpose? He needs a deeper connection to access how he can find meaning and happiness beyond material wealth. If a man can't nurture his emotional body, he may not embrace self-care and display robust health in his physical body. How can a wife place her trust in an insecure man with poor habits, tendencies, angry outbursts, and impatience? Will she put her faith in him if he is fighting with her when she is trying to nurture the family in the direction of health and wellness? She becomes insecure when she has to assume this role and oppose him. She can emasculate her husband and lose the inspiration to demonstrate her devotion and affection. Either one may only stay with the other to provide a stable financial structure. For a man in this situation, his creative energy becomes enslaved to matters of money, and for a woman, she feels unloved and alone.

A woman who empowers herself with equality and remains cooperative has balance. Genders must connect to the source of their Sacred Self and find a more profound sense of trust and faith in each other. My relationship with Sacred Self grew over time. I started to see it unfold and trusted the answers would come at times when I couldn't even anticipate what the questions might be. I was a single parent for twenty-six years and placed my trust in a faith based on everything I learned from yoga and my learning how to connect to source. That source was my touchstone for resolving stress and inner conflict. My life became spiritual, and the ordinary things I did daily became extraordinary. At times when I didn't know which step to take, I trusted the path would appear. I became entirely responsible for my health, my happiness, my decisions, providing for my children and providing for my future until I met a man who cared about his Sacred Self and together we could share an intimately sacred life of love and deep connection.

Today, I have a beautiful marriage and a successful blended family life with five children. Together with myself as the eldest, we span six generations which makes our family dinner discussions very interesting and unique. Statistically, second marriages and blended families are said to have a lower lasting rate than first marriages. Sometimes the breakdown is irreparable, and both parties are too destructive for one to begin to trust the other. However, if a woman can find her strength and connection to her Sacred Self, then she can open herself toward a reunion with her husband. She must be willing to find new ways to express herself without harshness or making him feel incapable of ever making her happy. I believe that if both partners can master stress, seek deeper intimacy, strive to be the best version of themselves and are willing to do the work of attaining this ultimate development, it is possible to beat the odds.

Exercises for relationships:

Men: Get in touch with your genuine feelings and tell your woman how you value, respect and love her. She will feel heard and begin to trust you as her partner. When you express feelings of appreciation towards her, the relationship can start to change for the better. Please try and see how her attempts to motivate you are for your highest good. Be willing to give her your best effort.

Women: Please remember that your man wants to love and cherish you. You have to be willing to be his inspiration and to express yourself in a way that helps him love you every day. Avoid manipulating him, making him feel guilty or humiliating him for this is a sure way to destroy his love for you. Be receptive to his need for love and affection and remember the bond of love is as strong as it is within you. If you seek to connect to yourself and your abundance, no emotional storm or offense can swing to take you off the course to wellbeing.

Contentment comes from a fullness that is cultivated through awareness and appreciation. Peace, joy, and satisfaction arise to bring a natural comfort that rests in having a deep connection to Self and others. The secret to happiness and comfort lies in your ability to connect and share simple pleasures with those you cherish. Material comfort is excellent too but does not compare to the lasting contentment that comes from the joy you bring to others through your contributions.

Communication Remedy

The art of listening and speaking from your heart requires the ability to hear the emotion behind the words. When you're an engaged as a listener you better understand the other person's viewpoint. You will also make that person feel heard and understood which helps to build a stronger and more profound connection between you both. I have found compassionate witnessing and actively listening to another's worries, fear, upset, and pain to be an essential skill. Some professional contexts for this communication skill include wellness counseling, mentoring, teaching and guiding others to name a few. Once you develop the ability to listen to others with empathy, then you'll need to acquire the ability to speak the best words, at the best time, in the best way, to get the best result. This complete two-way communication allows for more than the exchange of mere words; it provides for the transfer of love through heart-centered dialog.

The second aspect of communication is assertive expression. Being assertive means expressing your thoughts, feelings, and needs openly and honestly, while standing up for yourself and respecting others. It does not mean being hostile, aggressive, or demanding because assertive communication is always about understanding the other person. It's not about winning an argument or forcing your opinions on others.

I co-chair a committee that is lobbying for support on a legislative bill while also working with another group that is opposing a related bill. The fast-paced nature of working with statutory deadlines, sensitive issues and strong personalities who have different perspectives can create tension-filled words and sometimes hostile communications. It's important not to take anything personally, or be opposed to sorting through conflicting opinions. I like to stay centered and focused on facts that are stated in a way that is clear and to the point and not use language that is intended to persuade or force opinion. Sometimes one person might dominate the meeting. As co-chair, I make sure everyone is heard and aim to bring the group to consensus while meeting the objectives of the meeting.

The ability to be a good listener is the foundation of assertive speech. Everyone needs to know that their voice and concerns have merit, value and the right to be expressed. Not everyone can communicate with composure because they are passionate about strong opinions and have feelings behind asserting what they are protecting. Not everyone who speaks has integrity, and many try to manipulate others, lie in twisted half-trusts, or make negative judgments and bully with their words. It takes an experienced listener to sort through this type of word war.

Decades of practicing meditation have taught me to be constantly reflective of my thoughts and words. It has taught me how to witness my words with restraint. Meditation broadened my awareness of many things. It offers me perspective by giving me a macro lens to look at a microscopic conversation. The members of my committee elected me as co-chair because they trust my leadership and insights and know I will listen with full attention and consideration. I am respected in my personal and professional circles and have deep and caring conversations with my friends, family, and colleagues. There are a few who have learned that I can unravel twisted lies and can't be manipulated. These relationships take a very long time to come around with respect. There is also a balance between remaining emotionally neutral with restraint and expressing authentic feelings with sincerity. Every word counts — each mindful non-verbal gesture matters. You communicate not only with your words but also in your very presence of being.

Future Remedy

I see a future society displaying far greater maturity than our present community because people connect to the collective health consciousness and practice the art of wellness. As a result, they are versed in traditional methods of preventative medicine such as complementary medicine including yoga, meditation, herbs and lead a balanced lifestyle. They are innovative and use new biological discoveries for regenerative medicine. They do not have a thirst for power; instead, they have a passion for peace and goodness for the highest good. They are not weak and insecure; therefore, they do not lust after or aim to control or attempt to possess another to show dominance. They do not feel a need to use coercive manipulation and poor politics to influence another. This society believes in freedom, justice and finds a source of strength and a set of values which include a strong sense of family and global community. They consider the bonds in their tribes based on the acceptance and love cultivated through the cooperation of all.

Maybe we are at the end of an era of those who forgot what our ancestors and ancient keepers have been trying to pass on to us. As I approach my silver years, social imagination allows me to consider what it could be like to parent a planet, nurturing, guiding, awakening, setting firm limits, disciplining with appropriate consequences, teaching self-restraint without crushing a spirit or causing mental-emotional damage. People need to become more resilient to the effects of adversity and awaken the power of their discerning intelligence. This skill would help them to rise above disempowerment and navigate to a place of security that comes from inner freedom. Without attachment to greedy power or the need to dominate others, people will be free to support the highest good of all. Our world needs the total woman to connect to her strength and "be the remedy" for positive change.

ABOUT THE AUTHOR

KAREN NIELSEN

Karen Nielsen, an author, speaker and mentor, is the co-founder of Widow Women Connect, a sisterhood of widows who connect, support and mentor one another. Karen lost her husband Robert to suicide in January of 2018, and after his death, realized she had a platform to help others. Her life has given her a varied range of topics on which she speaks: overcoming adversities, finding your new normal, letting go of unwanted negative labels, suicide prevention, mental illness awareness, childhood sexual assault trauma and healing, placing a child for adoption, being a birth mom, and her personal battle with depression, anxiety and PTSD. Her first book, "Pathways: From Victim, To Survivor, And Beyond", was published in September 2018; her second book "7 Ways to Heal From a Loved One's Suicide" is due out Winter/2019. Karen and her Widow Women Connect co-founder Roni Ketchum are co-authoring "You Are Not Alone ~ Widow Women Connect", which details their shared loss, is due out Fall/2019.

Karen spent 30 years in the corporate world and only after her husband's death, did she fulfill a lifelong dream of writing and becoming an author. Karen is an encourager of everyone she meets, she loves to smile and laugh and has a zany, sarcastic sense of humor, a trait she learned from her Dad who she says is the 'king of puns and one-liners'. She has one adult son Chris, who she is delighted to call one of her best friends, and she currently lives in her favorite city on earth, Boise, Idaho along with the man in her life, a black cat named Puma.

You can contact Karen for workshops, seminars, keynotes and retreats at:

Cell: 208-412-6650
Email: Karen@karennielsen.org
Website: Karennielsen.org

SIXTEEN

When Loss is Personal ~ From Cradle to Grave

Karen Nielsen

Ten. I counted each perfect finger, each perfect toe, and there were indeed ten. I was basking in the gloriousness of holding my son, born just moments before on my 21st birthday, and I was falling in love with this beautiful little creature. I was thankful for any time to be with him, hold him, talk to him, as I knew it wouldn't last long and I needed to memorize every detail of his beautiful face, melodic voice and perfect fingers and toes. And I knew it would have to last me a lifetime. I had loved him with every fiber of my being for the nine months I carried him, but the woman he was to call Mom was not to be me. Although I had been sexually active since my late teens, I found myself pregnant at 20 years old, after one time of unprotected sex. I had spent years babysitting, not only my two younger sisters, but many other children as well, but I did not feel in any way prepared to be a parent. I was scared to death at what the future could hold for me, an unemployed failure of a girl, and I was also an absolute mess of a human being. So with the help and guidance of my mother, I chose to place my son for adoption.

The woman who would adopt my child was "Aunt" Suzanne, an old friend of my Father's family, and her husband Tyler, and they would name him Dillon.

Dillon and I were both still in the hospital after his birth; I was there due to a uterus infection and would be for three full days. Dillon was there as he was almost born breach, and in the process of getting him turned, the umbilical cord had wrapped around his neck. I was able to deliver him normally, but he was born a horrible shade of blue and not breathing. The nurses were able to resuscitate him, but that moment of not knowing whether he was dead or alive was almost more than I could take. It was like having him taken from me twice, and I was nearly hysterical, but hearing him cry literally gave a breath of fresh air to the entire delivery room and all its human inhabitants.

After the delivery, I was wheeled into a double occupancy room for the night and would be released a few days later after the uterine infection was under control. I was alone for the first few hours, glad for the stillness and quiet after the madhouse of 27-1/2 hours of painful 'back labor'. This is when the baby is situated towards a woman's back and literally puts pressure on her spine. The resulting pain, in addition to labor pains and contractions, is quite literally, excruciating. I was understandably exhausted, both physically and emotionally and I just wanted to have quiet, so I could sleep and recharge for the emotional battle that I knew lay ahead of me. But two hours later, quiet was not what I received as a new Mom and Dad were brought into occupy the second bed, along with their newborn daughter. Suzanne had told the hospital I was an "adoptive mom", and she had asked for me to be placed in a room alone, but that night had a full moon, so the hospital had to utilize every post-delivery room available due to being under siege by women going into labor. If you're asking yourself what a full moon has to do with all that, the gravitational pull created by a full moon doesn't just play with ocean tides, but it is believed to affect the amniotic fluid in a pregnant woman's womb. If the amniotic sac is under pressure, it can rupture, and contractions might begin. I always considered it to be an old wives-tale, but my due date was more than a week away, and there were 15 other unscheduled births that night, so its validity became very real to this former sceptic!

Let me tell you, two full days and nights of listening to new moms and dads loving on their newborns was almost more than I could take. It was heartbreaking to listen to them oooohing and ahhhhhing over their new little bundles of joy, while I lay there with my arms empty and weeping for what I didn't have. But I kind of felt the emotional trauma I was going through was God's way of punishing me for getting pregnant in the first place, at 20 and unmarried. My family was devoutly Catholic and the church's viewpoint on pre-marital sex could be summed up in one word, "No". This was also was the viewpoint of my parents, who had never so much as given me or my two younger sisters one word of guidance on sex or anything remotely connected. I grew up learning from my peers, and isn't that just exactly the kind of sexual education every parent wishes for their teenage daughter?

Let's back up a bit and examine just how I got myself in this precarious situation. I was 20 years old and had been at a party when I met Michael, "Mr. tall, dark and handsome"; at 24 he was an Armand Assante look alike, dangerously good looking and he absolutely screamed sex appeal. He was funny and charismatic and unlike anyone

I'd ever known, and that night began a six-month affair that rocked my young world. He had just come thru a divorce and had three very young children, so when he found out I was pregnant, he cut off all contact with me, left town, and I found myself all alone and scared to death with absolutely no idea what to do next. After talking to my parents, we decided to contact "Aunt" Suzanne, and she and her husband Tyler had agreed to my coming to live with them on their farm in northern California for the remainder of my pregnancy, and it was there I would put the child up for adoption and then return to my hometown of Boise, Idaho. But life has a way of taking our plans and turning them into something we never would have expected, and certainly couldn't have scripted. Suzanne and I had many talks during my first hours and days with her, and she asked if she and Tyler could adopt my child! Well this certainly changed the direction of how I saw all of it unfolding. And, as I told her about Michael and his family, she realized she had known his stepfather! She told me that he had been one of my Dad's best friends in high school and was also her first boyfriend, the first boy she'd ever kissed. It really was an amazing connection, and out of that connection she found Michael and was able to get him the necessary legal paperwork that he needed to sign.

Getting back to Dillon's birth and the subsequent hospital stay, the final afternoon that I was there Suzanne was going for a lunch break and her best friend Donna was taking the baby back to the nursery. The look on her face told me everything I needed to know: she didn't want me anywhere near Dillon for fear that I would bond with him. He was quite obviously out of sorts and had been crying for most of the two days since he had been born and his nurse had told Suzanne it was because he couldn't find me. I was the only voice, the only smell, the only human he'd ever known and now I was nowhere to be found in his tiny universe. Then Suzanne said and did something that would become one of the greatest blessings I've ever received, she asked Donna to hand him to me, as maybe I could calm him down. Donna didn't think that was a good idea, but she carefully placed the swaddled, crying infant in my arms. I touched his cheek with my finger, wriggled my nose against his, kissed his forehead, and in a soft voice said, "It's alright Dillon. You can stop crying now". His face took on a perplexed look for a moment, then his eyes got big and, I kid you not, he smiled. And he stopped crying. He just laid there in my arms, looking up at me with only that look a newborn can have for his mother, and other than the birth of my second child, this was the most profound moment in my young life. Donna stepped toward me to take him, but Suzanne stopped her, took her by the arm and led her out of the room saying, "Let's just give them a few minutes together."

I took what I had been given and spent the next ten minutes basking in the gaze of my son, knowing I would probably never have this chance again. I told him how much I loved him, told him how perfect he was, and asked him to one day forgive me for walking away. Those gifted moments with him were amazing, heartbreaking, and so incredibly bittersweet as I imprinted on my mind the feel of my son in my arms; the shapes of his fingers and toes and the feel of his skin on mine. The smell of his newborn baby breath was so sweet it was intoxicating, and I just wanted to breathe it in for hours. I stared at his tiny little nose and big, beautiful, blue eyes. Yes, you heard right, blue eyes. If you caught the description of his father and who he looks like, you'll know that Michael was part Italian with big brown eyes. A baby's eyes will change in time to their true biological designed color, but Dillon's stayed a denim shade of blue, just like mine.

Taking these few stolen moments to be with my son was a miracle I had been granted and they have remained imprinted on my mind. Afterward, as I placed my child back into the arms of the woman he would call Mom, the only thought in my head was "what in the hell have I done?" But that night as I lay there weeping, the one thought which invaded my mind over and over was, "What in the hell do I do now?"

In those moments, days, weeks, months and years after his birth and in my return to Idaho, I learned how to live without him. It wasn't easy. It took two long years before I stopped crying myself to sleep, and even more to assuage the guilt I felt for leaving my child. Adding to that, he was born on my birthday, so that day has been incredibly bittersweet with the memories of what I had done, but also what could have been. Let's put this in perspective, shall we? You can give up gossiping, you can give up clothes to a thrift store, or if you were raised Catholic like me you can give up candy for Lent. But none of that relates to a child, an actual human that you as a woman give birth to. You cannot simply give them up, drive away and never think of them again. But after giving birth to that miracle of life, you CAN lovingly place them in the arms of someone else who will raise them, love them, and nurture them throughout their lifetime. But placing your child in someone else's capable hands and arms through the adoption process takes a lot of guts, and it takes a lot of courage!

It took me a very, very long time and a lot of painful, guilt ridden years to understand how much courage it took for me to carry a child for nine months, give birth to the child, and then place that child into another woman's arms so he could grow up calling her Mom. The pain and emotional trauma that I went through because of that decision rocked me for years! I felt so guilty for not keeping my child as my own, raising him and loving him. But therein lies the crux of it all: I loved him more deeply than any human ever in my lifetime, but I did not feel that simply loving my child was enough. I was an absolute mess of a human being, I had no direction and honestly had no idea where to go or what to do with my young life, and I didn't want to raise a child in that confusion. I didn't want a child to pay for my mistakes, and I knew I would continue to make many. It was not fair to that child to live with a mother who had already made such a mess of her young life, and such a mess in fact, that I considered myself a complete failure as a human being at the tender age of 21. So, I chose not to keep my child as my own but placed him in the arms of another. Another woman, another couple, another family that could raise my child, love him and nurture him and give him all the things that I was absolutely sure I could not.

But 29 years later I would again hold my son in my arms, as an adult when he chose to meet me, his birth mother. Meeting Dillon was probably one of the absolute highlights of my life, and when we talked, he thanked me for giving him life. But he thanked me even more profusely for choosing the people who had been his parents, the people who had raised him, his Mom and Dad. Suzanne and her husband Tyler were absolute salt of the earth and listening to Dillon speak so highly of them and of his upbringing, I knew that I had made the right choice all those years ago to place him in their loving arms. Dillon and I continue to communicate through email, and it is a beautiful thing to have him want to be a part of my life, even in such a small way.

And I had also received closure with his father, Michael. In 2009 scrolling through Facebook, I found him and after collecting my thoughts, I sent him a message. He responded, and we talked very openly, candidly and very honestly about our past together and what we had created. We ended the conversation on a very positive note and wished each other well. It was the very best kind of closure I can think of with him, as it was final and complete.

The entire journey of giving birth to Dillon, placing him in the arms of another, and then walking away grieving the loss of my child, gave me a strength I didn't realize I possessed. I read a quote recently that spoke to me on how we as humans can choose to react to trauma and loss: "Life isn't fair. No matter what life throws your way, no matter how unfair it may seem, refuse to play the victim. Refuse to be ruled by fear, pessimism and negativity. Refuse to quit. Be a warrior and work through whatever life throws your way with courage, love and positivity. And continually push forward, because you are a survivor of the unfairness of life. You are stronger than you think. And you are cable of achieving far more than you believe."

It would be 32 years after Dillon's birth in which that strength would be tested and refined through a situation so devastating that the very foundation of my life, and of life's very meaning, would give me intimate knowledge of this quote and its lessons.

January 24th, 2018 at about 4:30 in the afternoon would be the date and time my world imploded. I came home from work that afternoon after receiving a text from my husband Robert telling me goodbye, and found him lying on our bed, dead from a self-inflicted gun-shot to the head. To say my world exploded doesn't quite give the enormity and gravity of what I experienced in that moment, and all the subsequent moments in the hours, days, weeks and months after. No, to be perfectly honest, my world imploded.

In September 2009, about six months after separating from my first husband, I met Robert at a 25 yr class reunion. We had gone to jr high and high school together in Boise, Idaho, and never met! Six months after the reunion we had our first date, and four months later we were married, in July of 2010. I don't think I ever realized a love like that existed, and at 45 years old, I truly fell in love for the first time. He hurt his back on a job site in November of 2012, and in May of 2013 had back surgery for a herniated disk. The surgery fixed the disk problem but left him with chronic pain in his left lower hip area, and that would lead to a myriad of other problems. He tried everything for pain from cortisone and lidocaine shots to opioids. Oxy Contin to be exact, and that is the little pill with the big side effects that caused a downhill spiral of overwhelming magnitude.

I had seen anxiety in him from the moment we met, but it was in the form of ocd on job sites, and him wanting to make sure everything was perfect for the customer. But after being on the Oxy Contin, his anxiety skyrocketed, and then came the dependency that rocked his entire body.

After about two months being on Oxy, we realized this was not the wonder drug the doctor had touted it to be and knew we had to get him off of it. We found another doctor who was willing to taper him down off the opioid, and it took four full months to do it! And that four months almost killed him, as not only was the drug still in his system but the dosage went down every two weeks by 5-10mg and it was horrifying to watch the with-drawl symptoms. He had the shakes like I've never seen on anyone, he was freezing cold most of the time, his anxiety was thru the roof with panic attacks the size of tornadoes, and he was in severe dire straits. In addition to all that, depression of some kind also seemed to set in and it was all I could do to get him out of the house. We had been told that after the last dose, it can take six months to a year for the opioid to finally clear out of your system, but I was not prepared in any way for what happened to my husband after the taper was over and he was no longer taking Oxy Contin, which was September of 2014. His depression worsened, his anxiety and panic attacks seemed to get worse almost daily, and there was something else going on that I just couldn't put my finger on. It was like his emotional status was being triggered, but I didn't know why or what was causing it. By October we had found him a counselor that specialized in helping patients with chronic pain, and she referred him to a psychiatrist who could get him on medication to help with the depression and anxiety. However, in January of the following year he seemed to hit a wall of emotional instability, and it was then that his counselor suggested he be placed in a psychiatric hospital in order to receive a proper diagnosis of what he was dealing with.

After going to the ER for a mental health evaluation, the doctor there agreed that Robert should be admitted into the psychiatric hospital, and it was 10:30pm when we got him inside the facility. They sat us in a small room by ourselves, and he was practically hysterical; they nearly had to give him a sedative to calm him down, and I wasn't much better. They took his shoelaces and belt because he was considered a suicide risk, then they took his clothes and dressed him in a paper shirt and pants. The only possession he still had were his socks and it broke my heart. He was crying so hard I couldn't understand a word he said, and I had to do everything in my power to keep my composure, because I couldn't let him see me fall. They gave us only ten more minutes together then asked me to leave, and as I walked out, I turned and looked at him, giving him the three fingered sign language for "I Love You". The forlorn look he had on his face nearly did me in.

As I walked out of the building and into my car, my body was wracked with sobs and I was barely staying on my feet, much less driving home. I felt I had completely let him down and he would hate me for leaving him there, even though I knew it was the best thing for him. I didn't sleep at all that night, and just before 6:00 am I received a phone call from Robert telling me he couldn't stay there, it was an awful place and as he had "voluntarily walked in" he could have left at any time, however their policy was that they wouldn't let him simply walk out, he had to have a ride. He said the only place he needed to be was home, with me. I told him to wait a few minutes; I had to talk to Carol, his counselor. This was not a decision I could make on my own and I needed her professional opinion, but I couldn't get through to her and Robert called back over and over as I was desperately trying to get in touch with her. I finally called her receptionist, who had become a dear friend, and after hearing what was transpiring, her answer was a resounding "NO, do not go pick him up." She said the doctor will be on rounds at 10am and Robert would have to wait until at least that time.

The next phone call I made was one of the hardest things I've ever done in my entire life. I had to tell the man who trusted me more than anyone else in his universe that he couldn't leave; that he had to stay. And he broke. He was sobbing uncontrollably and was nearly hysterical. I told him to just wait a few more hours for the doctor to come see him, and then he would need to abide by the doctor's ruling. Because he trusted me, he said he would wait and hung up the phone. That's when all composure I thought I had left me, and I was the one who was hysterical, crying so hard I could hardly catch a breath.

The doctor at the facility asked Robert to stay for a few days so they could try and figure out what they were dealing with and prescribe the right medications to help him. He ended up being there for an entire seven days, and it was so excruciating and overwhelmingly difficult for both of us, and by the end of his stay, the doctor didn't have just one diagnosis, he had three. Robert was plagued by Bi-Polar II depression, general anxiety mixed with social anxiety, and PTSD. I didn't even know there was such a thing as Bi-Polar II, but when I received the explanation, every box of what he was feeling, and experiencing, was checked. Bi-Polar I is the one most everyone has heard of and which used to be termed as Manic/Depressive Disorder. People with this disorder are either severely depressed or mile-high happy, there really isn't any in between. Bi-Polar II is a bit different. There isn't any mile-high happy on the manic side. For a person suffering with this disorder, there is no happy, no joy, no smiles, no laughs; only darkness. Only a low that is so debilitating, no light can enter. The "mania" for this disorder is depression, and the downside is deeper depression. Add in general anxiety, social anxiety and PTSD, and I realized he was an extremely ill man.

It was now early February 2015, and now that he was out of the psychiatric facility and home with diagnosis' and seemingly dependable medications, things seemed to settle down. But it didn't last long, and for the next two years it seemed we searched for the right combination of medications, the right cocktail if you wish. But the correct dosage and combination was extremely elusive, and Robert was getting restless. Without the medications correctly dialed in, his depression continued to spiral, and his anxiety was truly getting out of control. Near the end of that year, we even moved out of state, to beautiful, picturesque Walla Walla, Washington, so as to give him new surroundings without the visual of all the old haunts, doctors offices and customers he could no longer service. But even that didn't work, and after two years living away from family, friends and all things familiar, we moved back home to Boise. But what should have been a happy homecoming was short lived and turned into a nightmare only three short months later.

As I entered our bedroom that January afternoon and my eyes saw what my brain couldn't seem to comprehend, I screamed, and turned to run down the hallway and out the front door. I couldn't even stand in the living room of my apartment, it was too haunting and eerily quiet for me, so I called 911 and waited outside on the sidewalk talking to the dispatcher waiting for the police to arrive. Apparently, I had asked the dispatcher to send 'everybody', so she did! And you know what was worse than having police, firefighters and an ambulance arrive at my doorstep? Having the firefighters and ambulance leave after 10 minutes and not one of them could make eye contact with me. That act was so final, and it sent shivers down my spine, even more so than the January cold, as it told me that my husband was truly dead. I think even that moment may have been worse than actually seeing him lying there, blood everywhere, and his eyes, normally beautiful and hazel, but in death, silver and glassy in color, open but gone.

How do you comprehend that? How do you grasp the enormity and the finality of that? To think that my husband of only 7-1/2 years, the love of my life, my soul mate and life partner, would consider this his only option to truly become pain free, didn't make sense to me. Why? How? I looked back on the goodbye text he had sent me, which in part said, "It is time I step away and let you truly have a great full life without pain from me. I just want my lover to be happy."

He actually thought I would be better off without him! But that was really only part of it and I knew it, knew without a shadow of a doubt that he was so tired of being in pain, physical as well as emotional and mental. He was absolutely exhausted from fighting and getting nowhere in his recovery from the physical pain, and from the emotional toll of his mental illness. So, he decided to leave. But what he didn't realize is the toll it would take on me, on his kids, on his twin brother, his sisters and the rest of his family and all his friends. On all the people who loved him.

In the moments, hours, days and months since my husband's suicide, I have felt pain like nothing I could ever have imagined. For days I couldn't sleep, as all I saw when I closed my eyes was him lying there. I doubt I'll ever forget his eyes on that day. And for days I couldn't eat. I wasn't hungry in the slightest and food didn't interest me at all. And focus didn't come easy, everything was foggy and fuzzy for days, weeks, and even months. Family and friends gave as much support, encouragement, love and hugs as they could, but I learned they couldn't give me what I truly needed. Which was peace of mind. A friend of mine suggested I write a book, chronicling my journey in witnessing Robert's journey. So I did! And not only was it his story, it became my life story. "Pathways, From Victim to Survivor and Beyond" was published in September 2018! Writing every word, thought and emotion that Robert and I went thru in the years, months, weeks and days leading up to his suicide was so intensely catharctic, that I decided to write another book on all the steps that helped me survive. "7 Ways To Heal From A Loved One's Suicide" will be published in 2019 and will be accompanied by a journaling workbook to help the surviving family member or friend deal with the devastation of their loss.

How do you quantify losing the love of your life? How to you overcome the devastation? My faith in God, my family and my friends were the things that truly helped me in my darkest hours. And the overwhelming desire I had to inspire other people who are going thru chronic pain and/or mental illness, to not give up, to not give in to their darkness; and for the survivors, those that have been left behind, that there is indeed life after losing someone you love to suicide.

Loss of any kind, in particular the loss of someone we love, regardless of how, can be extremely painful. Sometimes we get stuck in the pain of yesterday, but what I've learned through the losses in my life is how to be present in today, in the here and now. As the late, great Will Rogers said, "Don't let yesterday take up too much of today". Living IN today and FOR today will bring more true contentment, peace and joy than I can even begin to write about in these short pages. Choose to be present, choose to survive, choose life! Namaste my friend.

ABOUT THE AUTHOR

H. B. COBINE

H. B. Cobine is a strategic initiatives consultant with over 10 years of experience in communications, strategic planning, relationship development, leadership development, and project management. She is currently a member of the Executive Project Management team for one of the nation's largest providers of diversified home and community-based health services where she designs and manages the execution of solutions to unique organizational challenges. An avid learner and believer in the mantra, the day we stop learning is the day we die, H.B. crafted her career path to include strategic positions across multiple industries. She has held positions in Academia, the Defense industry as a business development professional, and most recently the Healthcare industry.

A native of Cincinnati, Indiana, USA and graduate of Indiana University-Bloomington, and graduate of Indiana University – Bloomington, she considers herself a "forever Hoosier". After completion of her degree program she obtained a certificate in Non-Profit Board Management from the City of Bloomington, followed by a certificate in Alternative Dispute Resolution from Virginia Tech Polytechnical Institute. Her most recent accomplishment, graduation from the Fund for the Arts, NeXt Ambassador 6-month Arts Leadership program for up and community young professional leaders in the Greater Louisville & Southern Indiana Arts community.

Now a 5-year "Louisvillean" and advocate for bettering her community, H.B. has dedicated considerable hours since she moved to Louisville, Kentucky to learning the needs of her new community and how she can best serve. H.B. is a 5-year member of Junior League of Louisville where she has held various leadership positions, serves as a mentor to undergraduate and young professional women, attends Northeast Christian Church, and serves in volunteer and leadership capacities for other community organizations.

She enjoys traveling to visit her family in Indiana, exploring the out of doors, and spending quality time with her significant other (they can often be found in their gym or dining at a new restaurant – always striving for fitness and a balanced life).

Sharon, you helped me, and many others, understand our opportunities were endless (within reason), if we planned, put in the work, and faced our fears. Thank you for your support and encouragement over the years!

[signature]

SEVENTEEN

Shades of Our True Colors

H. B. Cobine

Introduction

While the idea of the authentic self appears to be a new age concept, evidence of this movement exists through the contemplations of Greek philosophers and in world renowned literature such as the Shakespearean classic, Hamlet. In Act I, Scene 3, we read, "This above all: to thine ownself be true, And it must follow, as the night the day, Thou canst not then be false to any man." (Mabillard). Look not far on your Instagram or Facebook feed for #liveauthentic and other similar hashtags, accompanied by a quote maintaining like it or leave it, I am who I am. Researching authentic living uncovered varying degrees and definitions of what can be summarized as *being oneself at all times*, *unchanging* due to circumstances, social pressures, at all costs being true to you.

Who, other than you, can decide who you are, and whether you are genuine? It is my belief we are able to maintain our authentic selves,

223

while projecting a side or version of ourselves that is best suited for our current environment or audience. Living with integrity, loyalty, and fostering genuine intent is not compromised by acclimating to our environment and audience or through life changes. This ability to adjust can also be assessed as adaptability - not inauthentic, fake, or manipulative as some claim.

A Cultural Obsession

One source of depression in modern Western culture has been tied to the often endless and disappointing road of chasing after an unyielding and finite personal identity. Introspectively, I wrestled with the concept of finding myself and discovering who I am until my current age. It was only recently I realized there is no earthly requirement for me to align on a set of personal standards and maintain each one in all relationships and circumstances. The restlessness we experience around not knowing whether we truly understand who we are, how to know, and even what to do if ever achieved is a manufactured right-of-passage like anxiety that our society has portrayed as a problem we need to solve. Moreover, proclaiming the lack of understanding your true self, makes you less of a complete person. Can you relate?

A contributor to the desire to understand oneself is the personality assessment industry, while hard to pinpoint an exact yearly revenue, estimated to be a $2 billion-a-year industry. Americans have become fascinated and even obsessed, myself included, with personality tests such as Myers-Briggs Type Indicator, Predictive Index, Gallup CliftonStrengths (formerly StrengthsFinder), and less professional or scientific based assessments found on Facebook and other social media outlets such as color-coded personality tests, what famous movie character are you, playing into the desire of so many to achieve total awareness of self. The desire to know our true being and how we interact best with others is so great, particularly in Western culture, that an entire industry is devoted to the marketing, administration, training, and expansion of personality testing.

The popularity of personality testing in American culture took off in the 1960s and has soared to unimaginable heights. Hardly a professional job application is written, office workshop strategized, or leadership conference planned without a nod to these tools to achieving self-awareness. When used as intended and ethically, these tools can provide tremendous value in learning how people with other personality types perceive us, how we best interact with others donning different qualities, and how to collaborate successfully. However, all too easily, an individual or a potential employer assessing a job candidate, might confine or be confined to his or her set of qualities defined by the respective test or assessment author.

For fellow MBTI enthusiasts, my results were extraversion (E), sensing (S), feeling (F), judgement (J), or ESFJ. An assessment for my personality type highlights characteristics people with ESFJ personalities likely possess including order, sociable, loyalty, personable, orderly, and more (MBTI Online). The assessment even provides a list of common and suggested careers for the personality type, none of which reflect my personal interests or career aspirations, suggesting my personality type would fare well in customer service positions such as a pharmacy aide, child care worker, or a medical secretary. In my career I am a strategy consultant, a leader in the organizations I work and volunteer for. I am not by nature a "supportive contributor" role as the assessment debrief suggests I likely am (MBTI Online). This illustrates perfectly my point, the danger of taking to heart and accepting that we must conform our identity to a human crafted set of expectations. To achieve the desired total self-understanding, individuals can and have adopted the results of these tests *as* their identity – instead of using the results as a professional tool. Furthermore, the live authentically movement suggests we confine ourselves to the box we have discovered or settled on that best defines us, within all interactions, at all costs, and in all circumstances – and any deviation of that is a false self, fake, and unauthentic.

Shades of Our True Colors

While searching for an editing tool to ensure I make grammatically appropriate choices in my contributing assignment for THE TOTAL WOMAN (admittedly I get carried away with comma placement), I discovered a commercial for a modern writing assistance tool called "Grammarly". Reading through the offerings provided on the product website, Grammarly's algorithms not only make basic punctuation and grammatical suggestions, they make style recommendations claiming to "help people communicate more effectively".

I decided against using the tool but am reminded of occasions during my undergraduate years at Indiana University when I asked my Dad to proofread essays and make style suggestions. The desire being to have a final product that exceeded expectations, an alteration from my everyday style. I can guarantee texts and emails to my friends were substantially lacking in the grammar department. I made a conscious effort to portray a more formal and educated version of my self through writing assignments, an entirely different representation than that I portray to friends and family.

Consider six groups of people you may interact with from day to day:

- Family,

- a Supervisor or Work Lead,

- a College Professor,

- a Stranger in line behind you at a grocery store,

- fellow Board members on a local nonprofit organization,

- and close Friends.

Reflect on a typical conversation, whether spoken or written with each group. What is your standard greeting for each? Would your text thread read the same with a group of close friends, as it would with a professional Supervisor or colleague? Would you greet a stranger at the grocery store with the same open embrace that you greet family members with?

Chances are, you adopt a different style of communication (sometimes unknowingly) to suit each audience, without sacrificing integrity of the message. We can adapt our interactions with varying audiences without sacrificing who we are. We can show shades of our true colors, while maintaining our individuality and what makes us unique. These differences in our communication whether written or spoken, illustrate our ability to adapt.

The ability to adapt is both a sign of intelligence, a sought-after professional quality. In the workplace, those who are able to set emotional reactions aside during times of adversity and logically plot a path to a solution are looked to as leaders. As the pre-Socratic Greek Philosopher Heraclitus wrote, life is "flux", our interpretation being, the only constant in life is change (Heraclitus). From the beginning of time to the present, our very existence and wellbeing was dependent on our ability to adjust to technological innovations and medical advancements. As we age, we generally do less of activities risking physical harm and take proactive preventative care, adapting to the reality of our human mortality. We seek professional development, updated certifications, and adult learning beyond our original collegiate experience to align us with changing career interests, or simply to stay relevant in our chosen field. Adaption is a woven throughout our human experience.

The same can be applied to our personal interactions. Let us revisit the interactions with the six diverse groups of people mentioned previously we encounter in our lives, even more so than adjusting our communication style, it is possible to project different versions of ourselves to each audience, to achieve a desired level of engagement and connection. Reflecting personally, when I am in a professional setting, I project a confidence I may not always feel – due to the nature of the work I do. Holding stakeholders accountable to strategic deliverables successfully often requires me to subdue my strongly empathetic nature and drive for results. One person may react to a style of communication, tone, or programmatic lingo very differently than the next. Managing a cross-functional initiative effectively requires consideration based on each team member's background when communicating. I would craft a different agenda or conversation for a Systems Architect, Communications Manager, or an Accounts Payable Specialist. The message is essentially the same, however tailored in a way to allow the intended audience to best receive and process the data. Integrity of message retained, different audience and approach.

Have you served on a Board of Directors for a non-profit organization, or taken a role in your community as a volunteer leader?

If so, you are familiar with the concepts of compromise, collaboration, and sacrifice of self for the greater good of the organization. As a Board member, decisions are slated for vote that affect organizational structure, finances, strategy, personnel, brand, donor stewardship, and other important business segments. When we sit at the Board table we put away ego and personal objectives in order to align with other members on the best path forward for the organization. Similarly, individuals who are not quick to provide input will step out of their comfort zones to provide needed information. In this instance, we are appropriately placating a portion of our total self to achieve the desired objective. If instead, Board members arrived at the table with a zero-sum alternative dispute style approach and competitive agendas, decisions made would be negatively affected, even poisoned, by the presence of ego or resistance to compromise.

The Science Behind

Studying Gordon Allport's years of research, one of the first modern trait theorists, we observe there are core attributes and personality traits that are not likely to change, commonly referred to as cardinal traits (Allport). These traits define who we are and shape our interactions and reactions. Central traits are the middle tier of Allport's theory, examples include honesty, shyness, and anxiousness. Central traits may be ingrained, but not unchangeable with conscious effort if the individual so desires. These traits influence, but do not determine behavior (Allport). The lowest tier is comprised of Secondary traits (Allport). Secondary traits are largely dependent on situation, and context of the interaction. The fear some feel when taking off from an airport runway is an example of a secondary trait.

Another modern personality model, first championed by D.W. Fiske (and further defined over the last 60 years by various Psychologists and Personality theorists), the "Five-factor theory", asserts all individuals are measured on a scale between two extremes of the following factors, Neuroticism, Extraversion, Openness, Agreeableness, and Conscientiousness (McCrae and Costa Jr.). Seemingly simple when compared to Allport's nearly 4,000 trait study, both theories assert a degree of transformation is possible across the human lifespan. Change in lesser traits can be due to age, environment, or concerted effort to create new habits within our being.

Scholars Jens Asendorpf and M.A. Van Aken offer "core characteristics are relatively stable traits that are largely immune against experiences in relationships and continuously influence their flux and flow. Surface characteristics are more open to relationship influences, and are therefore less stable." While there are unchangeable core characteristics of an individual, one should and cannot be expected to maintain a static existence in all circumstances. Living authentically, if defined as remaining unchanged throughout interactions with diverse audiences and in all circumstances spanning the human life cycle, sounds noble but is nearly impossible. Once we accept our conscious and subconscious practices of adapting to our surroundings, we are better able to monitor and truly understand our core personality versus the traits in us that can and do change. Scholars Robert R. McCrae and Paul T. Costa mirror my assertions, stating in their publication "Personality in Adulthood: A Five-factor Theory Perspective", "personality forms part of the enduring core of the individual, a basis on which adaption is made to an ever-changing life."

Changing Your "Self"

Often the best illustrations come from personal experiences, especially those that are difficult to share. I consider it admirable of bloggers and motivational speakers to use their personal stories, whether positive or negative, growth through pain, lessons learned, or joy of victory, to reach their audiences. We see ourselves in other people, we see our own truths in others' stories that help us know we are not alone in our life struggles. I did not think twice about sharing my story of change, hoping to resonate with someone who is going through a similar challenge, looking for encouragement to someone who has made it through – change is possible, even through the most adverse circumstances.

Following a demoralizing personal situation, I devoted considerable time to exploring the self I no longer knew. After years of downplaying and subduing my natural tendencies, I unknowingly had created a version of myself no one who truly knew me recognized. My upbeat, open, positive, excitable, talkative nature had been replaced with a shell resembling me in appearance, but afraid, closed-off, quiet, anxious, nervous, and opinion-less. Self-evidence that we can and do change who we are knowingly or not through exposure to different environments, relationships, life changes, and to adapt to our surroundings. After a period of soul searching, I thought I figured it out –I discovered a new self.

The self I discovered was self-absorbed and angry, projecting a confidence to the far extreme. I was focused solely on "self-love" and "reclaiming my time" two mantras fellow American Millennials will be particularly familiar with. I cannot fully explain why this was my reaction. This extreme came with a new set of consequences, equally as painful, mostly for people in my life I love and care deeply about.

If not for their patience and faith in me, there would have be a much different end to my story.

This new shade of me was not a form of myself I was proud to be, nor projected the type of person my faith calls me to be. I was raised in a non-denominational Christian home, fell away from my faith during that personal struggle, and reconnected years later. Once again, I set out to change – this time, with a clear mind and important lessons learned. I found a version of me that I recognized from better days, a smarter version displaying empathy, openness, integrity, generosity, and humbleness, that when I stripped away the jadedness of bad experiences, sadness, regrets, hardened hearts, thoughtless decisions, and disappointments over the years, shown through. Through growing in my faith and accountability by way of a loving relationship, I was easily able to see within me, the self I wanted to work toward and was proud to be. Daily, I continue down my path to a wholistic healthy self, mind, body, and soul. Do you think perhaps we are always a work-in-progress? Adjusting and adapting to best attain and achieve what it is we think we need or should be?

Transforming into a different version of you is not a simple undertaking. It takes time and intentionality to create habits, positive, neutral, or negative. First you must have a clear understanding of what it is you want to change. Consider carefully the reasons why you desire to alter something within yourself. Consistency is key to altering or adapting to simple habits such as waking up early to work out, to more complex habits such as a dietary overhaul, adjusting to the birth of a child, a new normal due to personal illness, or adjusting to life after the death of a loved one.

Talk with someone you trust. Lean on those who you know will be honest with you, even if it is something you do not want to hear. Consider a family member, friend, counselor, pastor, or life coach. Take time to recognize what in yourself you would like to change. Write or record your intentions, put together an action plan with milestones, and start working toward what it is you would like to change. Rely on the person you trust to hold you accountable to goals you have made. Empower your chosen confidant to speak up if they notice you regressing or falling off path.

Some personality scholars and psychologists argue we are stuck with a set of unchangeable characteristics making up our personality, like it or not – whatever hand the genetic card dealer dealt, is your destiny. Through personal experiences and witnessing experiences of others I wholeheartedly disagree.

Closing Summary

In closing, I leave you with a suggestion to focus less on chasing an exact definition of who you are. My research, assertions, and suggestions are that of someone with personal experience on the popular topic of personality. I have enjoyed sharing my thoughts with you. Living with authenticity in action, living with integrity, with loyalty, is possible without expending energy on over-analyzing your interactions to determine whether they are truly authentic to your true self. As you age, as you grow, as you meet new people, experience difference phases in your life, a portion of who you are will likely change along with those experiences.

Also, if you agree with my assertions, take comfort in knowing if there is a part of you that you desire to change, with a plan, determination, and accountability it is possible to develop new habits, even alter natural tendencies. Tomorrow, nor even the next hour is promised so I encourage you to enjoy life and make the most of each experience. Learn and reflect on the losses and failures and take time to celebrate the victories and successes no matter how small.

Works Cited

Allport, Gordon W. "Personality: A Psychological Interpretation". New York, NY: Holt, Rinehart, & Winston: 1937.

Asendorpf, Jens and Van Aken, M.A. "Personality–Relationship Transaction in Adolescence: Core Versus Surface Personality Characteristics". June 2003.

"ESFJ Myers Briggs Personality Description". MBTI Online. 2019. www.mbtionline.com/types/ESFJ/.

"FAQ". Grammarly. 2019. www.grammarly.com/faq#toc1.

"Heraclitus". Stanford Encyclopedia of Philosophy. Revised June 2015. https://plato.stanford.edu/entries/heraclitus/

Mabillard, Amanda. Hamlet. Shakespeare. Online.2018.www.shakespeare-online.com/plays/hamlet_1_3.html.

McCrae, Robert R. and Costa, Jr., Paul T. "Personality in Adulthood. A Five-Factor Theory Perspective". Second Edition. Guilford Press, New York 2003.

Notes: Read 11/12/19

— Thanks for sweet note

— Authentic self — we adapt
our communication of whom
we are speaking to.

— Personality tests are not the
end result but instead a tool
to look at careers but also
interest, abilities.

— We do have capacity to change
like your suggestion —
As a counselor, always believe
a person can change

— Like your honesty — we are
not alone.

ABOUT THE AUTHOR

DR. LaTonya Branham

Dr. LaTonya Branham currently serves as a college administrator with the rank of Assistant Professor in University Studies at DePauw University. During the span of her career in higher education, LaTonya has also worked at Sinclair Community College and Central State University. She is committed to advancing efforts that lead to optimum collegiate learning experiences, assessment, and faculty enrichment in higher education through scholarly research and professional engagement. LaTonya earned a Bachelor of Science in Organizational Management from Wilberforce University, a Master of Arts in Management from Antioch University Midwest, a Master of Arts and Ph.D. in Leadership and Change from Antioch University. Her research focuses on adult learners in higher education. She is a published author and supports various literary initiatives. LaTonya enjoys academic, career, and life coaching which she considers a wonderful opportunity to help transform lives. She is the founder of Reader2Leader Foundation, and Branham Consulting. Her motto is to "educate and elevate!" LaTonya and her husband faithfully support First Fruits community outreach.

Branham books include:

CultureSeek (1st edition, 2006 and 2nd edition, 2009)

Spirit Seek (2007)

The Academic Prayer (2013)

Contributing writer to *Chicken Soup for the Soul series: Devotional Stories for Women* (2009) and *Here Comes the Bride* (2012).

Contact:

Web: www.LaTonyaBranham.com

Email: LaTonya.Branham@gmail.com

Mail: Dr. LaTonya Branham, P.O. Box 1271, Dayton, Ohio 45401-1271

Social Media Profiles: LinkedIn, Instagram, Facebook, and Twitter

EIGHTEEN

Make Peace with Your Core

Dr. LaTonya Branham

I t's easy to say, "I'm not going to deal with this today." What happens when days turn into weeks, months, or years, and our inner core begins to feel unmanageable? Our inner peace becomes disturbed and we can either elect to ignore the situation or seek the path back to peace within our core. We have options and it is our individual responsibility to take advantage of all that it requires to lovingly massage our hearts and ultimately heal. Things, people, challenging decisions, mental or physical violations, or toxic relationships can attack your core in unexpected ways. At some point, we have to quiet our mind and return to a state of peace. Onward towards peace is easily said than done. Yet, its achievable!

The presence of peace is the absence of disturbance. It takes great effort to keep peace around us and especially within our core. Striving for peace within our mind, relationships, within our homes, schools, work spaces, and country are daily desirables – but not all achievable at the time when we need it most. As human beings, many of us are blessed to grow from childhood to adulthood, but rarely are we shielded from turbulence. Holding on to the bad things or decisions that happen in our lives is non-transforming. The journey to adulthood should be transforming and filled with peace. We can become our own personal peacemakers and it helps tremendously to have others in our peace camp so that we can enjoy the journey with minimal disturbance.

I can recall a time when I thought that transitioning from a fulltime job to becoming a fulltime adult learner in a doctoral program would allow me the time and space – minus the income – to fulfill a journey toward completion. I gave myself – through prayer – a year to complete the journey that I had begun two and a half years prior. Time passed quickly and a year later, I was still an unemployed student. I consulted occasionally, but not enough to satisfy my career and income goals. The sacrifices that my husband and I made for this journey began to overpower my confidence. Unexpected wait-time and diminishing faith started to impact what I had originally thought was a God-secured decision.

Uncertainty can be overwhelming and if allowed to happen, disappointment could squash my spirit and the inner peace that I wanted so deeply could begin to feel unachievable. It was never promised that we could get all of the answers to life's challenges. Yet, we have a significant role in how we handle challenges. Oftentimes, we tend to be intentionally rough on ourselves. Berating oneself is unsettling within the mind and inner core. It invites stress to take residence, and our emotional health begins to cry for healing – or escape.

I had to believe that finding my way to the light would brighten my core. It would be unfitting or unauthentic to present myself in any other way. I experience joy when elevating others, but for a moment in time, I blocked inner elevation for myself. Too much time had passed by and when I thought I was ready to return to academic life as an executive administrator and professor, the options were almost null. I began to question my decisions. Did God truly reveal to me that I could leave my job and then return to my career on "my time?" Bad decisions can lead toward the wrong direction. When this happens, it's time to re-calibrate so that what is considered a bad decision can turn into another life lesson. I now trust that it was not a bad decision, it was a re-directed plan that required faith and patience. Trusting the process – without self-blame – truly mattered in this case.

There was a brief period in my life that felt unfruitful and it pierced my core as if I was not worthy or that I had just run out of time to become more fruitful in my life. This felt like a form of psychological self-punishment – all because a year had passed and I was not receiving purposeful offers to return to my passion. Embracing or addressing mental toxicity or delving deeper in pain can be extremely uncomfortable – despite our outwardly pleasant appearance. Inner echoes of

"I can't do this anymore."

"This hurts – but just learn to live with it."

"I'm not good enough at this age."

"I don't deserve a better life."

"Are you ever satisfied?"

should be replaced with more positive affirmations and expectations that can bring peace to our core. One of my favorite quotes is "I am a daily contributor to my greatness and I deserve a better experience." There is power in positive affirmations. They reinforce your belief in yourself. Be an advocate for YOU! Create or find statements that affirms your value and feed your spirit. Allow it to become a daily ritual until you are convinced that you are worthy.

Your capacity to love yourself becomes greater when you are at peace within your core. Fill your core with self-love and appreciation – not only for yourself – but the love planted upon you by others who have your best interest at heart. My story was based on the attack of my self-confidence and diminishing faith with my career, education, and family financial decisions. There are other more penetrating issues such as being a victim of violence (mind, body, or spirit) that can puncture your core. Nevertheless, it must be addressed in order to heal and find peace.

Pause for Peace
(An exercise for the reader of this chapter)

How much do I love myself?

_____

_____

_____

It is possible to shift pain into joy, but it is unlikely that the experience of joy and peace will come overnight. I had to trust God's timing while re-learning to feed my mind with more positive thoughts about continuing and ultimately completing my journey. What I know for sure is that personal peace begins with you, but it's not all about you. The people who have touched your life and the lives that you have or will touch are a part of a more holistic experience. You are not only reconnecting with yourself; there may be others that you distanced yourself from because of your pain. It's your decision as to whether or not those persons are still needed in your life.

Your appetite for true peace should never starve, but things happen and it often requires the decision to reflect and re-direct. Reflection allows us to try to make meaning of the experience. Again, we may not receive all of the answers, but it's a starting point for owning the experience so that you can deal with the experience. When other people are involved, it may be necessary to begin the process without them. Remember, it's your core that is on a path toward peace. A professor once shared, "You have to show up for yourself." I honestly carry that statement with me every day because it is a confidence and ownership building affirmation. Discover what this means for you.

Pause for Peace
What can I do for myself today that will lead toward inner peace?

_____

_____

_____

Nurturing our core is critical for healing and rediscovering the best of ourselves as we overcome challenges that attack our inner core. Hurt and pain can be raw and itchy like a sore. Eventually the invisible "band aid" must be removed so that healing can begin. This allows us to heal and find peace. Are you self-guided or spiritually-guided? Your spiritual health is important. Prayer life, meditation, fasting, reading, peaceful walks, group fellowship, or other holistic methods of mental, spiritual, and physical nourishment can build the energy or strength necessary to get through turbulent times. Life's missteps can create internal barriers that may keep you from moving forward. Exercising your faith is important when there are circumstances, people, or things that you don't fully understand – things that you have NO control over. Let some things go and trust that life's challenges can be released to God for resolution. Faith is a weight-lifter carried by God – trusted by you. Life is filled with unexpected challenges that we must find a way to overcome in order to find peace. If you carry the weight, it will eventually overwhelm you and prolong the healing process. Gratitude is a good way to nurture peace. Focus on what you are thankful for and express it internally and externally. Gratitude is also a spiritual weight-lifter. It is the display of appreciation for life despite its challenges.

Another way to interpret the importance of nourishment is to understand the purpose of fertilizer. What type of growth is occurring while you are in pain, and what is possible while you are on the healing path? While the use of nutrient-rich fertilizer is great for plants, it is important to be mindful of the type of fertilizer used by yourself and others. Reject negative fertilizer that induces fear, pain, or self-sabotage. Living with hurt or pain is not essential to personal growth or healing – those are the type of nutrients that are negative. Positive fertilizer – injected through personal mental and physical exercises, affirming thoughts, prayer and meaningful external relationships are excellent keys to holistic growth.

Prayer and reading works for me because conversations with God allows me to pour out my heart with trust and give thanks for daily living. Waking up nurtures my core because it presents a new opportunity to breathe and engage in life. Reading elevates my mind and spirit in a therapeutic manner that turns into healing when necessary. It's imperative to encourage and nurture yourself to foster healing that will allow you to move forward. Reshaping your inner dialogue helps to control negative thoughts. It infuses affirmations that will lift your spirit and invite new thoughts or mental content to dilute the bad thoughts. De-programming from negative controlling forces can shift your focus to things you can control or manage without harm. If you were harmed by someone, a bad decision, or some unforeseen situation, it may require a spiritual lift to remove the trauma from your inner core. Prayer and meditation can add value to setting the tone for your day.

C.O.R.E.

Our core values are more than likely shaped by culture, experiences, and beliefs that often guide us through life. Even though we learn new things, the foundation of our core is a place that we can go to for comfort or guidance. When our core is disturbed or shaken, there are elements that are vital for the journey toward inner peace. They include:

C – Commitment. This means that it is better to stick with the process of obtaining peace. It's easy to give up, but there is nothing to gain when giving up on yourself. Commitment is also a promise to oneself that the investment is worth the journey toward transformation.

O – Openness and Ownership. Be open to the degree of transparency required for healing. Secrets might be revealed that could open old wounds or hurt others who never knew your story or situation. Secrets that hurt need to be released in some manner that works toward healing. The intent should not be to hurt someone else, but to help you get through the pain. Release the feeling of being a fraud – it's the path toward transparency. Once you take ownership in the role of your healing journey – and not the infliction of pain forced upon you – it becomes easier to have the burdens of your heart lifted. Surely, there are words, actions, or thoughts that we regret, but it behooves us to trust that regrets are forgivable. The act of forgiveness can be a bitter pill to swallow when you have been deeply hurt by another person or from a self-inflected wound. The pain can be unbearable; yet, it can also be released through "openness" and "ownership" to allow healing and nurturing to begin.

R – Reach. If you dig inside of your core at this very moment, what would you pull out? Would you be satisfied or disappointed – would it matter? Inner reach is important for the sake of authenticity and to reveal all of the fears that may have been hidden for too long. Once the inner process has taken place, then begin to venture outward with the comfort of self-care and supporting relationships. Don't take the journey alone. Reach out and align yourself with people you can trust enough to share your experiences with at any time. Even though visiting a psychiatrist may still seem taboo, it's highly beyond time to seek professional help when necessary. Seek recommendations and make a doctor's appointment that could someday change your life.

E – Experience. If you need healing within your core, it means that you've engaged – by force or approval - in an unfortunate situation. It's an experience that you didn't ask for; yet, you could still be living with the pain. The process of healing creates an opportunity for a new experience for yourself and others. As stated in the beginning of this chapter, days, weeks, months, and years could go by before we get the chance of a new experience. It is recommended that we take advantage of all opportunities to create a more meaningful experience... especially when it means stepping out of darkness and into new light.

When negative or unexpected things happen, why does the pain go straight to our core? Undoubtedly, it's the inner space that triggers the type of feelings and emotions that may or may not be displayed. Negativity or toxic behaviors becomes the reckless driver that could steer us in the wrong direction. At some point – after we are ready to face the issue – it becomes our responsibility to take back the wheel and drive toward a healing path to regain a sense of peace.

Pause for Peace
Create a positive affirmation statement that refills your core with confidence and joy.

_____

_____

_____

Other key factors that I've discovered through personal experience is that forgiveness matters. The importance of finding and embracing your quiet space and divine wisdom from people who may have already gone through similar experiences can add value to making peace within your core.

The Value of Quiet Space

It's necessary to block the "noise" and calm your mind. Your favorite room, prayer closet, or seat at the park could be a quiet space. It's the place to release burdens on your heart, in your mind, and to replace them with peace.

Trust yourself and be honest about your feelings. Things to do and consider while in your quiet space seeking inner peace can include:

➤ Quiet your mind to make room for positive thoughts

➤ Journal your feelings and expected outcomes

➤ Rebuild your self-esteem

➤ Own your current state

➤ Sort through your emotions

➤ Evaluate your attitude

➤ Build your level of confidence

➤ Renew your mindset

➤ Listen to the heart messages that soothes your spirit

➤ Build positive energy

➤ Focus on meditation and prayer to bring a sense of balance back into your life

➤ Prepare to reintroduce your best self

➤ Be mindful of your intake of:

➤ Food and drinks (dietary care)

➤ People (who has your best interest at heart)

➤ Conversations, thoughts, and music (focus on the positive)

➤ Places that are hazardous

➤ Adjust the amount of your intake. Too much of anything – good or bad – can be overwhelming or misleading.

Dilute those inner and outer toxic voices that tamper with your core. The environment and varying levels of conversation – depending on the people around you – should be encouraging and elevating. Encouragement is like someone watering your garden. Of course, that someone could be you because self-encouragement is a personal mental exercise. Encouragement from others can be that form of positive fertilizer that was shared earlier in this chapter. The feeling from encouragement allows an inner seed to finally grow into a beautiful blossom with a sweet aroma. Peace within our core is the aroma that we seek so that we can carry on through life in a more pleasant manner.

"Hope and fear cannot occupy the same space at the same time. Invite one to stay." —Maya Angelou

I concur with Maya Angelou's statement, but I would expound by recommending that fear be let go so that peace can join "hope." Hope sends us to a better place in our mind and hearts. It untangles the knot between the mind and heart that often prevents inner peace. The next level of good is better. It may be okay to accept the occurrence of an unfortunate situation, but it is truly better to make peace. We know that there will be set-backs, but we must work toward the next level to catapult our inner peace. Others can witness or experience your peace by your attitude, presence, speech, and actions. It is important to get rest, not just sleep, but quiet time to reflect and regain the positive energy that leads to peace.

Pause for Peace

Where is the best place for my quiet space and how important is it for me to quiet my mind to help overcome one of the challenges that is still clinging to my core?

_____

_____

_____

Be patient, but don't stall your healing journey. Our core is precious and it deserves daily care. We have to plug into ourselves to reconnect to the best of ourselves. There are times that we find comfort with waiting on God while ignoring God's guidance or a spiritual nudge that requires action. Remember to set things aside that are negative or eating from your core. Not that you can totally ignore it, but you can find a way to manage or resolve those matters that create psychological barriers... to the point that you can't think straight. We can't bring back lost time, but we can return to a state of peace. Be intentional about making peace with your core. This builds self-love and trust. The yoke of depression, fear, shame, and lack of self-confidence must be removed so that healing at the core begins to manifest signs of joy, elevated confidence, and ultimately – PEACE.

Notes:

_____

_____

_____

_____

_____

_____

_____

_____

_____

_____

_____

_____

_____

_____

_____

_____

_____

_____

_____

_____

_____

_____

_____

ABOUT THE AUTHOR

Dr. Jill Lee

I have been a business owner for over 41 years and have worked with people from all around the world and from all walks of life. Self-taught and diversified in every aspect of my manufacturing business, I learned it all from the ground up. I have interfaced with companies that were just starting out in business to some of the largest mega-corporations in the world.

One of the greatest rewards for me over the years was the opportunity to work with hundreds of loyal employees and thousands of clients. Every day brought a new challenge, and I was there, not only with an open ear but with an open heart. It is through these experiences that I had discovered my passion for working with others; to help bring balance, clarity, and harmony into their lives.

I then made a choice to take my life into a new direction and follow my passion. I became a Certified Holistic Life Coach, and earned my Ph.D. in Philosophy, as well as becoming an Ordained Reverend. With a thirst for knowledge, I couldn't stop there. I studied and received my Certification in Crystal Therapy and Crystal Healing. I am now studying for my degree in Holistic Nutrition, which I will incorporate in my practice.

It is now with great passion that I now work with many individuals and their families who have life-altering situations and challenges or looking to change directions in their life. I help others discover their strengths and guide them in a direction, so they can flourish in their own light, and live their best life.

Author of: Fifty-Two Weeks of Clarity: How to Transcend to Self-Reliance

Co-Author of: The Assertive Woman: Confidence, Communication & Charisma

Co-Author of: Tapping Into Your Inner Beauty: Let it Shine From Within

Co-Author of: Madam President: How to Think and Act Like a Leader

Co-Author of: Leaving Your Baggage Behind: Letting Go of the Past and Healing for the Future

Co-Author of Leading From the Heart

Co-Author of Breaking the Concrete Ceiling

Contact:

Web/Blog: http://www.lifecoachwithheart.com/

Mail: Dr. Jill Lee – 2416 W. Victory Blvd. #122 – Burbank, CA 91506

Telephone: 1-818-859-6104

Email: jill@lifecoachwithheart.com

Facebook: https://www.facebook.com/HearttoHearts1

NINETEEN

Holistic Wellness

Dr. Jill Lee

What is holistic wellness? Holistic wellness entails "wholeness with self," Mind, Body, Soul, and Spirit ~ as it becomes aligned and harmonized. It's more than a day at the spa, and a superb lunch after; not to say that that isn't a wonderful beginning, and not to mention enjoyable!

Self-wellness begins with loving yourself entirely from the inside out; caring enough to make conscious choices, which lead to mindful changes. It's also about creating healthy lifestyle habits that will help you stay in control, of not only your health but your entire state of being; which includes your mind and spirit. Balance involves all aspects of your life. When you create balance in your everyday living, you find yourself with an abundance of energy to meet life's challenges.

Healthy minds can enjoy greater peace with clarity, again, leading you to make better lifestyle choices; bringing results to a healthy spirit. You are then able to connect with your inner self most deeply, as you begin to develop a beautiful relationship with "self" while strengthening your relationships with others.

As we age chronologically, our body ages right along with us. I do believe that we all desire to live a happy and healthy life as long as we are here on this earth. But to live this balanced life, we must become aware of the connections between mind and body. If there is an imbalance, your body will speak to you. Do you listen? Can you recognize the signs?

Be reminded that even though our bodies and minds work very hard, we are not machines. We are living and breathing cells that need to be cleansed, nourished and cared for. There are times when we just need to shut it down, unplug, rest and recharge. *Easier said than done...right?*

I personally made a choice many years ago, to do just that. Love myself healthy. I took inventory of all areas of my life. I sat myself down with pen and paper in hand and asked ~

Do I have self-love? Is my heart open?

What do I see when I look in the mirror? Am I happy with what I see?

Am I healthy and physically fit? How are my eating habits? Do I get enough rest and sleep?

How do I feel emotionally? Do I hold on to anger and resentment? Can I forgive?

Am I calm and grounded? Do I overreact when I should just respond to situations?

I answered each and every one of these questions, plus more, and acknowledged each of my answers. There were many behavior patterns and habits that needed to be modified, and so I did. I made a conscious choice to change the direction in all areas of my life.

I examined each answer and reflected on my lifestyle patterns. I set new goals and planned each task so that I was able to achieve each one. As I chipped away at each quest, I became empowered to keep going.

But to create this balance and harmony in your life, we must also understand what it is that we are balancing, and so I have provided you with a brief summary of Mind, Body, Soul, and Spirit:

The Mind

The mind as we know it; is the core of our body. It's what creates communication and interaction between soul and spirit. It's where one becomes aware and engaged with "self," where you can register feelings, emotions, or any other impulses that may come about. It's what enables you to process the world around you and each one of your experiences. The mind processes conscious thought; for you to think, feel, and to make the choices that will have a direct impact on how you live your life. The mind brings about self-awareness, and again…the ability to choose whether to neglect or block out what you may not want to feel or hear. The mind enables you to listen, not only with your ears but with your heart and soul.

We live in a world with chaos and turmoil that often affects our daily existence. It often interrupts our daily routines and disrupts our ability to think rationally, clouding our vision.

When you begin to quiet your mind, you become the receptor of information and knowledge. Your inner voice speaks to you quietly. Listen, as this will help you look and see beyond the obvious, if only for a few moments, and look at life as it's happening, though a different lens. You gain clarity.

And it's with clarity, you begin to dissolve away toxic emotions or anything that may be holding you back from living your best life, while at the same time making room for your "Zen" or "Happy Place" within. When you free and open your "mind space", you allow life to touch you ~ as you live it, in the most beautiful ways.

At the end of the day, as you quiet and empty your mind of daily debris, you nourish and prepare for tomorrow. Take a few moments to listen to your thought patterns and feelings, while asking yourself, *"where did these feelings or emotions come from?" "What do my emotions convey?"* Questioning and knowing is called *"Emotional Intelligence."* Recognize and follow the signs. Living with negative emotions can clog your heart space, and leave you without an opportunity to receive new blessings into your life. It fills your mind and your heart space with the wrong kind of emotions and leaves no room for happiness, joy, love, or peace. _

Remember that your brain is responsible for all of your senses, including movement and thought. Thoughts and emotions are connected to manifestation. Keep in mind, that *your conscious choices* will create harmony and balance for your mind, body, soul, and spirit. Balance and harmony ~ so you can experience joy in everything you do.

The healthy foods you choose to eat will also help support your day to day routines and activities while repairing cell damage in your body (which you may not even know about.) Unhealthy choices can be the host to an array of medical issues, such as obesity, diabetes, cancer, cardiovascular disease to name a few. All of these issues affect your mind as well as the body.

Pay attention to how you feel after eating particular foods. Do you feel energized or lethargic? Understand that there are healthy options to replace every unhealthy choice. Proper nutrition is a pathway to good mental and physical health; it's one of the most significant forms of self-love.

So when you change the way you look life, you change your thinking patterns and begin to change life as you live it. How you look at life, and how you react to what's happening around you, allows you to move beyond and rise above those less than happy times. It's all about clarity.

Begin to quiet your mind, as it becomes the receptor of information and knowledge. Your inner voice speaks to you quietly. Listen as this will help you look and see beyond the obvious, if only for a few moments, and look at life as it's happening, though a different lens.

You are in charge ~ know that you can make mindful lifestyle choices that will *help create a new daily routine for your well-being.*

The Body

*The body is the outer shell that protects your mind and soul; it's the physical part of our being, which houses our spirit. **According to Wikipedia**: "A physical body is an identifiable collection of matter, which may be more or less constrained by an identifiable boundary, to move together by translation or rotation, in 3-dimensional space."*

The physical body's flesh, bones, muscles, and internal organs must be nourished and cared for to survive; cared for, from the inside out. The inner body; while quite complicated; possesses all the necessary systems for regeneration, rejuvenation and rebuilding itself. It's your responsibility to care and nurture it ~ as it's the only one you've got. It's essential to provide your body with the right conditions, mentally, physically, and spiritually, so it will function at its optimal level.

Eating healthy doesn't have to be a chore. It doesn't have to be boring, and you don't have to deprive yourself of the foods you love to eat. It's more about bringing healthy choices into your eating lifestyle. You may be quite surprised when you start becoming aware of what you're eating and how you feel after you eat.

Do you often walk away from the table and say *"Oh ~ am I stuffed!"* or *"I ate too much!"* Perhaps you don't say anything at all, but you leave the table feeling ill. Not a great feeling ~ I know! This can all change by making simple, yet mindful modifications to not only what you eat, but how you eat. How and what you eat plays a significant role in your mental, emotional and physical well-being.

Bringing natural foods into your diet is of the utmost importance if you want to obtain and maintain optimum physical and mental well-being. Yes, your emotional and mental well-being are tied to your physical health and your dietary choices. There are many more healthy superfoods that you can incorporate into your diet, Change it up, and get creative. Begin to modify slowly, and keep incorporating a little at a time. It takes time to change, and when you go slow and steady, you are more likely not to go back to your old habits.

You have choices. You can continue wishing you had a healthy body, or you can choose a healthy way of eating to obtain optimum results.

Here are a few modifications to consider on "how" you eat:

1. Watch your meal portions. No need to measure, just eat enough to where you feel satisfied, not full. Listen to your body.

2. Incorporate more color into your meals. Yes ~ meaning more vegetables, foods from the earth. **Green, Red, Yellow, Orange, and Purple.** *It's not only appealing to the eye but can taste good as well. 51% of what's on your dish should be plant-based. (Below is a list of rainbow foods and their benefits)*

3. Limit your refined sugar and table salt intake.

4. Limit processed foods, (Tran's fats).

5. Eat slowly... take your time and chew your food well.

6. Eat healthy snacks throughout the day.

7. Limit wheat flour. (Read your labels)

These are only suggestions to help get you started. Take a look at the foods you eat, before you eat them. Ask yourself. *"How am I going to feel after I eat this?" "Is this good for my body?"* If the answer is *"yes"* and you are going to feel good ~ then go for it, and enjoy. If the answer is *"no,"* just realize that you have options. Perhaps you need to make a different choice. If you still choose to eat whatever it may be (this guilty pleasure) eat a smaller portion, so you don't feel deprived, but you are satisfied. It's about learning to modify your eating habits and becoming mindful of what you put into your body.

It's always a good practice to plan your meal times. Of course, situations change, so do the best you can. Choose or create an environment where you are relaxed, perhaps with family or friends, while engaging in pleasant conversation. Listed are a few other tips on how to eat mindfully.

- *Never plan your meals when you've had an emotional upset when you're stressed, angry, or bored.*

- *Recognize your hunger signals so you're not eating emotionally.*

- *Make sure your seating is upright and comfortable. Never eat lying down.*

- *Be mindful of your breath patterns, which you may need to bring yourself to a place of calm, before enjoying your meal.*

- *Relax your stomach muscles.*

- *Feast your eyes first, then inhale the aroma of your prepared meal.*

- *Begin to enjoy the taste, as you chew slowly. Pause between bites.*

- *Recognize when you have enough to eat.*

Only when we become mindful of our eating patterns, can we change. It's a choice that belongs to you. You may ask why?

The benefits of eating mindfully

- *You're able to enjoy the flavors and aromas on your dish*

- *Reduces food cravings*

- *You tend to notice when you've had enough to eat, avoiding what's known as "food hangovers"*

- *You tend to eat slower, therefore digesting your food so you can get the most of the nutrients*

Mindful eating is about paying attention to the foods you put into your body and the effect they will have on you, both the inside and outside. It's not about judgment or criticism, it's not about comparing yourself to others. It's about witnessing the sensations as you eat and digest your food. This awareness helps you to make better choices for your well-being.

The Soul

It's somewhat difficult to describe the soul accurately. Let me try ~ The soul is the "I" or "Self" of the physical body or also known as the life of a person. It's an immaterial essence, that is responsible for giving the human body its spiritual life force; and is driven by love, inner wisdom, and service of the Universe. The soul directs your moral and emotional behavior, guiding and influencing you to make the choices, which best serve your well-being.

Just as dirt, dust, and grime can attach itself to those mentioned above physical things, the same happens to our souls. No ~ not dirt and grime ~ let me explain.

Often we can find ourselves faced with tough decisions or choices, which can bring upon stress, worry, and anxiety. There are times when there are adverse reactions to life situations. We may be in the company of those who exude negative energy. What we read, hear and watch on television, radio, or social media also play a role in how we feel, and when negativity sets in, our soul absorbs it like a sponge. It all becomes toxic to our well-being. You may not notice or realize this right away, but believe me, it's there. Those feelings of fear, guilt, frustration and even immediacy set in and begins to stifle your decision making, resulting in losing your inner balance, clarity, and peace.

By indulging in self-love, you can begin to experience the results almost immediately. Mindfully, try to avoid processed foods whenever possible, especially those with refined sugars and sodium. We all have that "sweet" spot that needs to be satisfied. Choose foods that are naturally sweetened, such as fresh fruits. Make your meals like the color of the rainbow, so it's not only tasteful but pleasing to the eye. We do enjoy food with our eyes first. And, whenever possible, choose foods that are organic and without GMO's.

Eat mindfully for the purpose of nourishing. This brings about calm. And as an added bonus, clean foods will enhance your spiritual awareness.

Remember that it's the soul that directs your moral and emotional behavior, guiding and influencing you to make the choices, which best serve your well-being.

Unhappiness and negativity is a *disease of the soul*, for, without peace, there is no calm. Recognize and get in touch with your feelings. Allow this state of tranquility to come to you, through the consciousness of "self" and be at peace with who you are.

The Spirit

While both soul and spirit are a non-visible force, there is a difference. Humans "are" a soul, whereas humans "have" a spirit. The spirit is the non-visible character of the soul. Both, however, are the center of your emotional experiences and both affect the human body. Your spirit also relates to your beliefs and is an open awareness in all areas of your life. There is no right or wrong in your beliefs; it's personal for each one of us.

The Human Spirit, according to Wikipedia is *a component of **human** philosophy, psychology, art, and knowledge - the **spiritual** or mental part of humanity. ...*

The human spirit is what brings our body to life. A simple comparison would be - our body needs spirit as a radio needs electricity. Spirit is the source of power that is beyond the confines of our physical body and; yet, is the most intimate part of our being.

It can be quite challenging, realizing and maintaining an inner balance, especially living in a world which can often continue to spin around us, creating chaos and havoc. But it's balance that keeps us grounded and with peace. It's balance that allows our inner light to shine. It's balance that helps to keep our hearts open and full, yet light through adversity.

The only way to maintain our balance is to continually cleanse and nourish. Being present, in this very moment, will allow you to do just that. Being conscious of your thoughts and actions, through each experience will bring you to a place of "knowing."

Your expressions bring about emotions that lead to transformations of self, opening your heart space. By being conscious of these expressions, feeling your feelings, channeling and releasing your blocked energy, you can create a life well balanced and harmonized within your mind, body, and spirit.

Mind, Body, Soul, and Spirit Aligned and Harmonized

As previously mentioned, this is the circle of life. There are bridging components that contribute to the flow of energy, in every area of our life. We must have a complete understanding of how these elements all work together in harmony so that we can live our best life. For the mind, body, soul, and spirit cannot function well without this alignment, and it is this alignment that creates balance and harmony in our life. So let's explore each area of Mind, Body, Soul, and Spirit so that you can enjoy your current state of "being."

Mind, body, soul, and spirit are all connected ~ it's our responsibility to create our own internal balance. But again, what does that look like for you??

It's not always easy to find and create balance. With our day to day busy lives, with all of our responsibilities and obligations, it's so easy to let lost, in ourselves. When this happens, we miss out on special moments that may be happening in our lives. This isn't deliberate, it's because we are humans living in "auto pilot" mode. What to do?

We can't compare our lives with one another, for what is busy and hectic for one, may not be for the other. However when you make the time to step back and pause ~ when you make the time to truly pay attention to what's happening in this very moment, a new world of possibilities open for you, in all realms of your life. It becomes an awakening, and not only changes your life but changes how you look at life and it changes how we live our life.

Raise your vibration and create a healthier ~ more positive lifestyle.
Cultivate and practice forgiveness ~ compassion ~ gratitude
and empathy ~ Self-love first ~ and love ~ always
—Dr. Jill Lee

Notes:

ABOUT THE AUTHOR

MELINDA J. KELLY

Melinda J. Kelly is the author of Finding Your Coach Diving Deep Within, contributor to The 1000 Ripple Effect, What We Love, and The Professional Woman 2018 Anthology. Her professional life has been with her family's business Francis B. Kelly & Associates, Inc., known for publishing and business counseling. A 4th generation Los Angeles native, she has been involved since childhood with Las Primeras Guild of Childrens Hospital Los Angeles; Junior League of Los Angeles, serving on their Board of Directors multiple times; and with her fraternal organization Alpha Omicron Pi International Fraternity serving as a local, regional and international officer during the past four decades; and in leadership of several other organizations specific to the Southern California area.

Through her professional and volunteer experience, Melinda realized that much of her life was involved in 'the Question,' and embracing the power within every question we encounter. Her writing deals with looking at the norms we have accepted while looking at the lives we thought we would lead. Questioning our paths and our choices for success or happiness, can often show the inner truths and values, leading us to our best dreams and life.

In her private life, she is thankful for friends everywhere and is happy to travel near and far. It seems that her travels take to palm tree friendly places - Palm Springs, Florida, Hawaii, Mexico, the Caymans, the Caribbean, Brazil. There is a reason her friends refer to her as the hothouse flower. In summer you will find her at a concert under the stars or in her garden.

Melinda is a graduate of California State University, Northridge receiving a Bachelor of Arts, English, with post graduate work at both CSUN and UCLA.

This is her second collaboration with Professional Woman Network. Her next book is scheduled for a 2020 release.

You can find her at MelindaJKelly.com or follow her on social media at melindajkelly

TWENTY

Dance to the Beat of Your Own Heart

Melinda J. Kelly

W hen first presented, this was about marching to the beat of your own drummer. But as I thought about it, women move to their own music within. Men (and some women) might enjoy marching about, marching to orders, marching into battle, but it struck me as a phrase with such a masculine energy and feel. Standing in line, Muzak playing overhead, most women without even thinking about it tend to sway, hips gently moving to the external and internal music about us. Holding a child, we automatically begin to sway, to move, to rock.

Music has been associated with the sacred, the ritual, the celebration, the story. From time's beginning society has divined methods to tell the tale of our being, our history, our traditions, our rituals. Dance is within every element of our day, with or without the compliment of music. If you have ever stood waiting for an item at a busy service counter, particularly a restaurant that specializes in takeout meals, there is an elegant ballet of placement, of spatial awareness, of body positioning, that allows many people to flourish in a small area, fulfilling customer needs, working with hot items, sharp objects, and breakable items. Yet they move about in this elegant dance unaware of the ballet and balancing act they are performing, and more importantly, that we often don't recognize as such, or fail to see.

Where does such balance and grace come from?

One might say it comes from the every day actions of women. Through the days, decades, generations, millenniums, we have passed this gift to one another. It is part of our DNA. Think of the first two women sharing space within a cave. If they weren't careful with the placement of the fire, they could suffocate. If they weren't careful with the placement of the fire, they might freeze. Or lose the fire – and therefore warmth – to the wind, the rain, or other elements. When they were cooking, the need for spatial relationships was paramount. Too close we might burn ourselves. Too far away, we might freeze, or at least be cold. And if cold, we might get ill. And if we burned ourselves, we were subject to the possibility of injury, infection, and death. Our primal mothers taught these new lessons to their young, and kept the chain of people going and growing. It opened our eyes to the importance of our being, and being in the best, right or safest place.

As we moved from subsistence hunting and gathering towards nurturing safe crops, our way of teaching these lessons changed. We had the time, and relative safety, to develop a more fluid way of telling our tales. Looking at cultures from Mesopotamia to China to India, tales with music and motion, became a way to tell the masses stories, histories and as written language developed, the way to impart information. The Hula is a language to those who have studied it.

Each nuance of the hand implies a different meaning. As Polynesian Islanders traveled, they needed a way to greet, explain, share, warn, talk. The language of dance allowed them a universality we have for the most part forgotten. Any tourist in the day who went to the Honolulu Kodak Dance Pavilion was treated to a lesson on the roots of Hula and its multiple levels of meaning.

Capoeira is another form of movement disguised as dance that has multiple layers, meanings, and dimensions. Started in the disguise of dance, it was a way to keep African religious traditions alive. It was a way to stay physically and mentally strong when fearful slave owners did not want to allow their 'workers' access to written word and communication. The dance became a way to share information with the nuances of movement, the traditions from their native country, and a way to defend themselves when they did not have access to any sort of weapons for defense.

It is hard to not appreciate the Indian – native American and Indian nation – for the majesty and storytelling of their dance. Again, with music or not, with a simple drum beat or chant or song, people from differing areas could find their common ground and communication. With the Native American tribal dance, we most often think of the warriors in full headdress, regalia and often warpaint as they perform their most majestic and powerful dances. But each dance had meaning from welcoming warriors home from the hunt to welcoming the coming of spring. With a deep connection to nature, dance celebrated nature in its entirety by the community.

With Capoeira, we think of the men in white pants and sashes with meanings, defying gravity and the laws of physics, as they perform their art for our amusement, now seen as entertainment. Yet we think of women when we talk of the Hula. Elegantly attired in grass skirts, floral leis, and wreaths in their hair, gently, elegantly moving their hips in ways to convey meaning, with hand gestures subtle and grand, becoming the 20th-century face of Hawaii. So too the dancers of India, whose roots in dance go to the Sanskrit and B.C. While there are several elements, they all convey the spiritual and communication truths of the dance through prescribed gestures. The colonist who first saw it confused it with the tales of the Kama Sutra, mixing the message of an ancient nation, with ancient ritual, and ancient tales, missing the meaning. Like its sister dances, it has meaning above what modern missionaries saw or interpreted as lurid sexual movement. Equally misunderstood was the art of Belly Dancing. It is believed Belly Dancing came about in preparation of women for the process of giving birth. The control and awareness of each of the abdominal muscles, their relationship to the pelvic floor, the body core being continually strengthened prepared women for the act of childbirth, recovery from delivery, and the ability to return to the business of their daily life. At a time when many children supported a family's ability to till the soil to raise food for storage and usage, maintain animal stock, and assist the family with the older children, usually girls, raising the younger children, a mother and wife in good health able to recover quickly from childbirth and step into her daily life was a necessity, not a luxury. The value of a healthy partner is still seen in many parts of the world, where the entire family supports the continuation of the family collectively.

So perhaps begins our obsession with our hips. Our derriere. The reference to a woman with child birthing hips. A woman who could provide many children to a man. If wealth and continuation were dependent on a large family, a woman who brought that 'hope' to the marriage was a catch. Yes, many of us know wide hips might mean many things, but they became the symbol of a fruitful woman, and therefore, a desirable woman. So begins our obsession with the magic zone below the waist, seen as a place of possibility, of a man's dreams of legacy, the continuation of his name and seed, the source of wealth and workers. A place of power. A place of possibility.

European dance was confined to the intricacies of dance steps, limited motion, and a partner. Dance changed from expansive and open to limited and with conditions. Women lost some of their ownership and yes, even their power in the dance. Yes, it could be said that downstairs the dancing was wild and lusty and full of energy, but when the energy and aspirations had climbed the stairs, they refined and made more delicate, precise, sanitized steps, that became the new, and stilted strange norm of dance. Our joyful innate connection had been altered to a less enthusiastic approach to something that had been part of our birthright. It's easy to see how the European colonists of any country were appalled by the wild gyrations (by their standards) that made up the cultural dances wherever they landed. European dance had become reduced to conventions limiting women to the invitation of a man to participate, following a prescribed set of steps and a ritual disconnected to the music. Dance became about parading for social purpose not primal enjoyment. The city-folks and titled souls danced the Minuet while their country cousins did a Virginia Reel. The differences of one's station separated us rather than joined us as they had done for centuries before. Until one might say, a worldwide group of young people threw these relatively new rules and regulations and painful limiting expectations and with their privilege threw convention out the window. Youth reclaimed dance.

The 20th Century seems to be marked by women throwing caution to the wind and re-embracing the joy in their bodies, the joy in their hips, the joy of dance. The Flappers with their short hair, short skirts, and Charleston didn't need anyone. The music started, the gin flowed and the dance began. Perhaps it was the cataclysmic events preceding the '20's, but life was for living and they were going to live no matter what. The world had survived the chaos, unfathomable chaos, and the sense of urgency and life and the moment was upon them. So was jazz, gin, and new freedoms represented by cars, jobs, votes, and momentum unheard of previously. Everything was exciting and the music might have been manic but so were the times. It is so interesting to think that in a short amount of time dance would go from exhilaration to drudgery as the Depression and marathon dances and dance hall girls took the joy from dance and made it a form of work, desperation, and impoverishment. This sad time of dance was short-lived, yet lives on in language and lore. The rise of musicals with elaborately choreographed sequences where the dance told the tale of seduction, the depth of emotion, and the lightheartedness of the moment helped people escape the realities of their day to day life. It also opened the doors for people to be professional dancers in a way not really known before. Dance was a limited professional option and art form. The advent of mass entertainment, the formation of ballet as an art form, the more egalitarian nature of burlesque and vaudeville, the Ziegfield Follies, the rise of the film industry, and musical theater of Broadway created a new line of work. Chorus girls, actress, background dancer all became ways for women to be gainfully employed. Oddly though, dancers and theater people were not always given the respect the profession deserved. It gave hopes and created work that had never been there before for the masses. Dance again changed, and in changing offered new possibilities to those who embraced them.

It took a second war to return dance back to comfort, affection, liberation, and expression. Combined with the exuberance of the music, dance became a way to bond, to share, to express the longing and love and hopes of a new generation. Sending a soldier away with the last dance, coming into town on leave and finding some gals to dance with, dance became a social currency that allowed anyone and everyone a moment together. A moment together to dance, if nothing more. A language unto itself, something that could provide the reasons to fight for and come home to.

Dance has continued to morph in a relatively short amount of time in many ways. Dance became an exercise of manners and social construct again juxtaposed with the athleticism of jive and sock hops. One need only think of films like Grease. Or the social etiquette of the country club dance as both social ritual and business diversion. Dance became more egalitarian and could replace conversation when needed. One's ability to dance became a much greater social need. You could get away with being awkward or clumsy before. It would be covered in the constraints of the dance. Now it was much more freeform and therefore challenging and innovative.

Women began to reclaim dance. Reclaim our natural birthright. Instead of waiting to be selected to dance, we returned to our original dance steps together. In our camaraderie, our sisterhood, we heard the call of the music and wanted to move. Needed to move. We felt the music within our being calling to us to move to the notes and rhythm. The music and the times gave women the comfort and confidence to dance alone, dance together, dance with abandon, dance with joy. When the music called, we no longer waited for someone to ask us to dance but instead answered the call of the music and the response within. It marked a return to our roots, our heritage. And it is wonderful.

Dance again has the power to calm the savage breast, can be used to exorcise personal or romantic demons, often used to charm others, turned from an art form to an athletic endeavor, the language of seduction and love, the devil may care tease of first love, dance to honor nature, dance to cheer the soul, dance to purge the unwanted, dance to cleanse our hearts, dance to bring the rain, dance to celebrate. Dance again is in the hands and the hips of the women who love and nurture her best. Dance is again the universal language that we share with one another, no longer removed from others but shared with all. Dance as our joyful birthright has come home again and when the music begins, from the moan of the wind to the babble of the stream to the clatter of the kitchen to the percussion of machines, our hearts alight, our pulse quickens, our eyes widen, and slowly, softly, subtly, our hips begin the motion and movement they have known for the millenniums, and we dance. We dance to the beat of our own hearts.

Notes:

ABOUT THE AUTHOR

PHYLLIS S. QUINLAN, PHD, RN-BC

President of MFW Consultants To Professionals, Phyllis is a successful nurse entrepreneur. She has practiced as a legal nurse consultant since 2004 and is a sort after lecturer and keynote speaker. During her nursing career, Phyllis has practiced in clinical, education & administrative positions in a variety of clinical settings.

As a certified transformational coach, she specializes in the unique needs of nurses and other healthcare professionals struggling with the emotional impact of compassion fatigue and the challenges of career transition. She is committed to working with organizational leaders in the creation of healthy work environments.

Phyllis is also the career coach for the Association of Perioperative Nurses/ AORN. She regularly presents on a variety of topics for 3M Healthcare.

Phyllis has authored three books:

Rediscovering the Joy of Being a Nurse: A Holistic Approach to Recovery from Compassion Fatigue

The Delicate Balance: A Mindful Approach to Self-Care for Caregivers

Bringing Shadow Behavior into the Light of Day: Understanding and Effectively Managing Bullying & Incivility in Healthcare.

She is very active on social media and regularly posts on her Blog, LinkedIn, YouTube Channel, Twitter, Facebook, Tumblr and Instagram sites.

TWENTY-ONE

Addressing Bullying and Incivility in the Workplace

Phyllis S. Quinlan, PhD, RN-BC

My specialty is not the management of disruptive behavior. My practice-focus as a certified professional coach is the management of the consequences of unrecognized compassion fatigue (formally known as burn-out) upon professional and family caregivers. Over the last fifteen years or so, I have coached hundreds of fine, empathetic individuals who give their heart, knowledge, and skills to care for their fellow human beings. It was during those coaching sessions that I began to realize how much an unhealthy work environment factored into the level of distress my coaching clients were battling.

Many things can factor into creating an unhealthy work environment. The issues can range from work-life integration demands to staffing issues, to dysfunctional work systems. However, each person shared with me that laboring under the constant stress of toxic behaviors demonstrated by nursing colleagues, inter-professional colleagues, or leaders was the most difficult challenge and factored greatly into the erosion of their physical and caring resilience. The focus of this chapter is the assessment and management of the disruptive behavior of bullying in the profession of nursing.

IMPORTANT GUIDANCE

Under no circumstances should an individual decide to take on a bully alone. The safe, effective management of bullying behavior can only be achieved if there is a close collaboration between Administration, Human Resources, and Management. In those organizations that are working under a collective bargaining labor agreement, Human Resources should be partnering with Labor as well.

To take on a bully alone is dangerous and reckless. The thinking and actions of a bully are often very aberrant. It is nearly impossible to outthink a bully on your own. You may leave yourself wide open for the counter charge of engaging in harassment or being labeled as a bully yourself. The most professional and prudent course of action is to partner with those I have mentioned and collectively agree on a course of action. Otherwise, you could unwittingly damage or even destroy your career and reputation.

What Does Bullying Behavior Look Like?

Bullying is a shadow behavior. Most of the transgressions are subtle. The wrongdoings are often committed out of the sight of those who could witness it or be in a position to stop and escalate it. However, if the bully perceives themselves in a position of power and therefore, in their view untouchable, bullying behavior can be openly condescending and observed.

The Workplace Bullying Institute maintains that bullying is a pattern of abusive horizontal or vertical conduct that can be verbally or physically intimidating. It is important to denote that bullying is a pattern of persistent behavior to distinguish it from an aberrant, one-time indiscretions that can be exhibited by anyone under the right circumstance.

The American Nurse Association shared that between 18 and 31 percent of nurses reported experiencing bullying at work. In 2017, the ANA published pocket cards outlining other examples of bullying behavior in the workplace. These examples include:

- Being yelled at or screamed at in front of others

- Being accused of errors made by another (scapegoated)

- Being the subject of gossip

- Being the subject of rumors

- Being humiliated in front of others

- Being consistently assigned undesirable work Being sabotaged personally or professionally

- Having critical information withheld that can impact job performance

- Having your opinions, thoughts or feelings ignored or belittled

Shining Light on Our Complicit Behavior

As I traveled across the country in 2016 speaking to nurse leaders on this issue, there was agreement on several points addressing disruptive behavior. The nurse leaders estimated that 85% of their nursing staff demonstrated the practices that align with showing up to work ready and willing to do the right thing. These staff members report to work committed to delivering high quality of care day-in and day-out while maintaining a civil work atmosphere. It followed then, that the remaining 15% of their staff members are those who exhibit consistent, disruptive behaviors. There was also agreement among these nurse leaders that, of this troublesome 15% of staff members, those considered to be chronically uncivil made up 10% of this number. That left the percentage of disruptive staff members who exhibit actual bullying behavior at 5%.

Conventional wisdom tells us, that as leaders, we should be able to get our arms around 5% of any issue or challenge with reasonable effort. If there was a 5% spike in patient falls with injuries, avoidable pressure ulcers, or any other nurse-sensitive quality metric, we would have a corrective action plan in place within hours. Why then are we challenged in putting an effective strategy in place when it comes to the 5% of disruptive staff members exhibiting bullying behavior?

The answer to this question has several aspects to it. First, we have incredibly knowledgeable and skilled colleagues that devote their professional energies to the advancement of the care of patients with behavioral health issues. However, given the choice of caring for one emotionally disturbed patient or a busload of multiple trauma patients, nurses are going to choose the trauma patients.

We are not comfortable, let alone as skilled as we need to be, with the management of aberrant behavior. We prefer to address care issues that respond well to antibiotics, chest compressions or restoring a patent airway. Managing behavior is challenging and time-consuming. It is often unpredictable and can require incredible patience.

Managing aggressive behavior can trigger anyone to feel threatened and at risk. The continuum of responses can range from meeting fire with fire to regression, and peacekeeping tactics. Given the typical workload on any given workday, it is not uncommon for leaders to prioritize addressing staff behavior issues at the bottom of a very long list of things to do. Many leaders will opt out altogether preferring to insist that those involved manage the problems themselves.

However, a significant part of the answer lies in our very caring natures. We are professional caregivers. We are nurses and nurses never admit defeat! There is always one more thing we haven't tried or a bit more energy we can invest to make a difference. Here is where we become part of the problem instead of part of the answer.

When someone shows us their true colors, we consistently try to repaint them. Have you ever made an excuse for a staff member's bad behavior? Have you ever told someone on orientation that you are going to buddy them with someone who can be a handful but if they (the orientee) keep their eyes open and mouth closed they can learn a lot? When did public relations manager for disruptive colleagues become part of our ever-expanding role?

A bully (narcissist with a license) is counting on just this kind of ingrained peacekeeping response to remedying an uncomfortable situation. There is a reason why bullying thrives in the industry of healthcare and more specifically, in the caring profession of nursing. Narcissists not only need to surround themselves with willing givers but, they must be around people who are willing to give until it hurts. They need people who can be counted on to move the finish line, explain away, or accommodate the bad behavior. Acknowledging this excessive caregiving, co-dependent trait in ourselves is the first step to rethinking our approach to managing the toxic 5% of our staff.

Excessive caregiving usually appears as the tendency toward being helpful to everyone. We help family and friends often without being asked. We help staff and coworkers even though they can handle a task or situation themselves. We get so caught up in the act of being helpful that we forget that nurses were never intended to fix things. That is not our mission. It is not our purpose to be helpful. Nurses are meant to be therapeutic. Being helpful promotes dependency, not independence. Our good intentions interfere with a person's ability to change, adapt, and grow to accept the reality of a situation. When we choose to be helpful instead of choosing to be therapeutic, we begin to flirt with the behaviors of enabling and co-dependency. We keep people stuck. We become complicit.

As nurse leaders, we must compassionately accept that, in many cases, we have been complicit. The goal of peace at any price is far too high a price for the majority (85%) of staff to pay for showing up to work daily. They endure the disruptive behavior, watch our actions, and pray that we will eventually do the right things. They have been patient and disappointed for far too long.

The Nature of a Bully

I think the best way to start this discussion is by raising our awareness of the nature of a bully. I submit that the disruptive behavior we label as bullying is the mentality and noxious temperament of a narcissist in action. Let's exam the personality disorder profile of a narcissist to gain some insights into the thinking and motivation of a workplace bully. According to the Diagnostic and Statistical Manual Disorders (DSM-5), published by the American Psychiatric Association, narcissism is a personality disorder characterized by the following personality traits:

- An exaggerated sense of self-importance and demonstrating an arrogant, superior manner.

- The belief that they are unique and expect people to defer to them because they are special.

- Expects recognition without notable achievements that warrant attention.

- Believe that they are superior and can only be understood by equally excellent individuals. Therefore, they intentionally and consistently ignore the chain of command and feel empowered to go directly to upper management or administration.

- Possesses a sense of entitlement and expects special considerations and accommodations.

- The callous lack of concern for the needs or feelings of others.

Bullies (narcissists) often act with the demeanor of someone who is incredibly self-secure. This false confidence is camouflage for the fact that the bully is in constant battle with their fragile self-esteem demons. What confidence they have is superficial and cannot withstand scrutiny, let alone criticism. They react to criticism as if it were a physical threat. Their response goes beyond the conventional reaction of denial, defensiveness, and perhaps anger. It triggers their need for retaliation and revenge. This need for retribution is referred to as narcissistic rage.

Narcissists do not form or sustain commonplace personal relationships. They exploit people. They view people from a *how useful are you to me lens*. They create and maintain a relationship based on how beneficial that individual is to their personal agenda and readily terminate the connection when the usefulness or benefit no longer exists.

The Narcissist's Secret Weapon

It is vital that you understand the secret weapons of a narcissist. They are proficient in the art of manipulation. They commonly possess above average intellect and are usually highly skilled at what they do. They count on these characteristics to create the perception that they are indispensable. You often hear others share that these individuals are difficult to work with, but they are great at what they do. This admission gives the bully/narcissist confidence that you will hesitate to definitively address any indiscretions or disruptive behavior because you require their knowledge and skills to help the department operate smoothly.

Perhaps the most unsettling secret weapon is that they frequently possess the following predator characteristics: attractive, charming (when they feel it is a useful tool), and seductive. They can tell you exactly what you want to hear. If you confront them with their disruptive behavior, they can often make you believe that they are truly sincere in their desire to get it right if you give them one more chance. This ploy is used to get the person in authority to move the finish line and unwittingly enable the behavior to continue.

They are cunning, clever, and very capable of distorting reality so that you question your own judgment. This ability to manipulate facts and influence perception is another reason why it is essential that you never try to address the behavior of a bully alone. They are masters of polarizing people. Remember that the bullies can restate lies or half-truths as facts. They are brilliant at talking over and around a conversation until, in the resulting chaos, you look like the aggressor and they look like the victim. A partnership between administration, human resources, and management is the only safe, professional approach to addressing this staff member's behavior.

The Cycle of Disruptive Behavior

Bullying is intended and predictable. At some point in our professional nursing careers, we were all trained in the cycle of abuse. Whether the topic was domestic violence, elder, or child abuse, the predictable cycle was the same. There would be an event followed by a period of expressed remorse and promises of reform. The abuser's behavior would be repentant and perhaps overly kind for a time. This time is the latent phase of the cycle. But this reformed conduct cannot be sustained. Over time, the abuser, would again become irritable. People around the abuser and the potential target would start to become anxious in anticipation that another event was imminent. Regardless of how those around them tried to accommodate and appease the abuser, something would eventually trigger them, and another incident would take place.

This cycle is the same pattern of behavior exhibited by a (narcissist) bully. Their inability to have self-awareness and empathy for others overwhelms their ability to self-manage and sustain any claims to turning over a new leaf. The bully declares that he or she is not responsible for the new occurrence citing that they were provoked and insisting that the reason for the most recent event lies with someone else. The bottom line is that the bully's behavior is predictable and follows a pattern. The bully is incapable of sustaining any stated guarantee of reform. Expecting a narcissist to change and comply with a plan that serves the greater good is foolhardy. Those who have been laboring under the toxic behavior of a bully know this. Those individuals sit, wait, and hope that leadership will come to this undeniable conclusion and become the champions of change before irreparable damage to the unit morale or a significant patient error occurs.

So, What Is the Solution?

As you might expect, the solution to a complex, multi-dimensional problem is also complex and multi-dimensional. The protocol for addressing bullying behavior should include but not be limited to:

- Offering intense training to leaders designed to educate them in the nature of a bully and the consequences of unrecognized, unaddressed bullying behavior upon their staff and desired clinical outcomes.

- Design user-friendly documentation tools for managers and leaders to easily access and capture aberrant behavior in a uniform and timely manner

- Require that disruptive behavior and the interventions used to address it are reported monthly by all department heads and human resources.

- Authorized staff intervention, aimed at bringing attention to the aggressive event, in your policy, procedures, and training sessions. Entitle it the *When You See Something, Do Something* intervention. Make it clear to everyone that the Human Resource Laws address Zero-Tolerance are real and enforceable. The is go a long way to minimize the *Bystander Effect* that can cause witness to bullying behavior to ignore or accept it.

- Invest in a Culture-Change Program to revitalize the benefit and importance of civility in in the workplace. Reframing your language to declare that every staff member is far more than an employee. They are citizens of their department and organization. With citizenship comes responsibility and accountability to live up to the requirements for such citizenship status.

- Commit to training everyone in the four competencies of emotional intelligence. In this way, administration is acknowledging that in the 21st Century, academic knowledge and clinical skills are no longer enough to ensure a successful career in healthcare. You must also be self-aware enough to be skilled at self-management and building collaborative working relations.

The time to draw our line in the sand on this issue is now. We must find the will and the voice to say something when we see something. This commitment will take the confidence and mental toughness that is the hallmark of tenacious leadership. Insisting on civility and the maintenance of a healthy work environment is at the heart of safety and patient-centered care. It is a fundamental pillar of transformational leadership. We owe it to our patients, their family, and the silent majority of civil staff members within any healthcare organization to be unwavering in this pledge.

References

American Nurses Association. (2017). Tips for nurses dealing with incivility & bullying. http://www.nursingworld.org/ Bullying-Workplace-Violence

American Nurses Association. (2015). Position Statement: Incivility bullying & workplace violence. An online article retrieved from Google on the World Wide Web. http://www. nursingworld.org/DocumentVault/Position-Statements/Practice/ Position-Statement-on-Incivility-Bullying-and-Workplace-Violence.pdf

Ariza-Montes, A. (2013). Workplace bullying among healthcare workers. International Journal of Environmental Research & Public Health;10:3121-3139

Bartholomew, K. (2006). Ending Nurse to Nurse Hostility: Why Nurses Eat Their Young And Each Other. Marblehead, Maine: HCPro, Inc.

Ethceverry, S. (2013). The Bystander Effect. John Darley and Bibb Latane's experiments. An online article retrieved from Google on the World Wide Web. https://prezi.com/edknk_8ivzvj/ the-bystander-effect-john-darley-and-bibb-latanes-experiments/

Healthy Workplace Bill: http://www.healthyworkplacebill.org

Joint Commission. (2016). Bullying Has No Place in Healthcare. Quick Safety Bulletin, Issue 24.

Goleman, Daniel. (1998). Working with Emotional Intelligence. New York: Bantam Books.

Goleman, D. (2001). The Emotionally Intelligent Workplace. San Francisco: Jossey-Bass.

ABOUT THE AUTHOR

JUDITH CARMODY

Judith Carmody is an Educator, Author and Speaker. An International Consultant with exceptional knowledge on the dynamics and contexts of bullying behaviour based on her books **Co-Bully No More and Unwrap the Gift of YOU.**

Judith's books are in the University of Maynooth, Trinity College Dublin and University of Oxford, England. In 2019 she gave a presentation on The Bystander(s) at the World Anti- Bullying Forum. Her book Co-Bully No More is on the literature list of the International Association Workplace Bullying and Harassment. (IAWBH).

Judith is an appointed International Advisory Board Member and a Member of the International Speaker Bureau PWN Louisville, KY. In 2018 she gave a powerful presentation to a standing ovation at Professional Woman's Network Conference, Louisville and at Ireland's Health & Well Being Week 2018. She co-authored FINDING YOUR VOICE: The Assertive & Empowered Woman 2017. All books published with Professional Woman Publishing, LLC.

Judith is a CPA, (Certified Public Accountant) with a Masters Degree in Finance. She completed Train the Trainer - Bullying Prevention and Intervention in Dublin City University. She uses her experiences in the private sector, public sector, corporate workplaces and industries in Ireland, Boston and London to explore social, communication and human resource systems.

Judith is an advocate for best practices in bullying prevention and intervention. One of her greatest rewards is supporting those who have experienced or are experiencing bullying behaviour. Judith encourages each step towards light and love, creating awareness of self-care and self-protection in a sacred place.

Contact:
Website: www.judithcarmody.com
Email: info@judithcarmody.com
Linkedin: www.linkedin.com/in/judith-carmody-author
Twitter: https:www.twitter.com/judithcarmody1
Facebook: www.facebook.com/authorjudithcarmody1

TWENTY-TWO

Intelligence in the World of Work

Judith Carmody

"Intelligence is defined as the ability to acquire and utilise knowledge"

Well Done! You are successful in your application for that new dream job, or maybe you are applying for your second job! You feel happy and YES, it should be the most exciting time in your life. You've spent years in education and further years gaining qualification(s) in your desired field. As everybody knows, to achieve and be successful it takes hard work, time and dedication. You committed yourself to education and achieved a degree or doctorate, then a good job is a pay-off and a well-deserved right. In your first job, you were lucky, you worked in a professional, fair and healthy company. Your company recognised your potential, encouraged and inspired you to be the best you could be. You achieved what you wanted to achieve with the dedication you invested in your chosen career.

Manipulation in the World of Work

But one day, a new manager starts and the dynamics change. Now there is an air of oppression, suppression, omission, and dismissal. He/she diminishes your role, ignores your work and liaises with a colleague for your area of work. When you try and discuss your position, he/she tells you he/she "is busy" or "I will get back to you soon". So, time moves on, and you are either fobbed off or ignored. Your former role is no longer attainable, you feel isolated and diminished. What do you do?? You report your concerns to your line manager as you believe this situation can be resolved but over time your fears are ignored. There is an atmosphere of confusion and mixed messages. It becomes for you, a place where you feel, you are not supported. There are hints that your post is no longer safe. Comments for example "why do you work so hard, take a tea break", or "the only reason you got that job, is because you know Jack" or "there is no future for you here". You begin to doubt your abilities and you no longer feel safe.

Demeaning Behaviour in the World of Work

Your line manager doesn't communicate with you or include you in meetings. The hierarchy support the line manager or have little interest in your welfare or survival. You inform other managers but it falls on deaf ears. You are told to "toughen up", or "I find him/her alright", or "stop playing the victim". There is no support for your situation and the management do not STEP UP and resolve this issue. Your workplace becomes for you a personal crisis of values, justice and trust.

So, how can you prove that you are being diminished and bullied in the workplace? You are caught in a very dangerous vulnerable position. Someone is manipulating the situation to suit and better themselves. A coercive atmosphere and controlling behaviours are now in place. Coercive or controlling offences can be classed as similar to those experienced in domestic abuse and violence. They are debilitating, underhand and dangerous.

> ***Coercive control is defined as ongoing psychological behaviour, rather than isolated or unconnected incidents, with the purpose of removing a victim's freedom.***
> —Sophie Goddard

• Unreasonable demands	Underhand and manipulative behaviour
• Negative focus on the target	Degradation
• Restricting daily activities	Threats or intimidation
• Monitoring of time	Watching and restricting movement,
• Controlling abusive behaviour	Taking personal items or entitlements
• Demeaning the target's character	Gossiping about the target

So the game begins, with little or no sympathy or support for the target. The target's health and financial survival is under threat. A target must develop self-awareness skills if he/she is to survive in this underhand, devious and toxic environment. Bullies have developed a very devious underhand way to succeed at the expense of a target.

They have little or no thought for the target's WELLBEING. Their obsession is to "GET RID OF OR DEMEAN THE TARGET". Targets now must develop smarter skills called intelligence in the world of work and OUTSMART the bully.

Let's go back to the beginning of your Employment.

On commencement of your employment you signed a contract of employment. The terms include the **duty of every employer to provide a safe workplace.** However, if you become a target in the workplace, bullying is not covered by actual legislation unless you can prove the company is negligent in their duty of care. The onus is on (you) the employee, to prove, that you have been bullied.

Under the **Health & Safety Act 1989**, *an employee has to prove that an employer did not protect an employee in the workplace.*

The company on the peripheral appears to be completing their side of the contract by having policies and procedures in place. However, in a lot of dysfunctional workplaces the policies are only in writing. These policies do little to actually protect the target.

Policies and Procedures in the Workplace

1. Dignity at work (including anti-harassment, anti-bullying and equal opportunity)

2. Health and safety

Employees are well advised to ensure clarity in their employment relationship with their employer. There must be an open discussion and understanding on how policies promote a safe working environment.

Address policies that do not create a safe workplace. For some, this work system becomes a nightmare, an unsafe place, a place that by-stands when their employees are under personal attacks on their premises and under their roof. One of the basic fundamental rights of a human being is a **"feeling of safety"** and if that is threatened it becomes an uncompromising dangerous environment.

According to statistics, a lot of bullying is undeclared and covered up. It is inaccurately recorded as illness, not fit for work, early retirement, moved or demoted. It should be legally recorded as *HAD TO LEAVE DUE TO UNRESOLVED PERSONAL ATTACKS IN THE WORKPLACE.* There is a disturbing silence about the attack, despite the target's obvious physical disappearance. Management stood by, didn't step up, support or resolve the attack. While life goes on as normal for all others, **the target's life, career, health and financial stability is destroyed.**

Are the powers in place, so indifferent to the chronic emotional distress, suffered by a target? Are they so oblivious to the personal, financial, health crisis that is happening? Is the destruction of a human being acceptable under their Contract of Employment? Is it customary to continue without questioning, what happened to a contributing qualified employee? Is it okay that the bully(s) continue in the workplace without being confronted or reprimanded for their abusive behaviour? Is it normal that the bully is rewarded and promoted following personal attack(s) on a target(s)?

It is imperative there is an in-house education, support and programmes that implement safety into practice. It is vital to have a **workable safety policy** that protects employees from abuse. Many employees struggle in unsafe environments. I want to reach out to those who feel unsafe, unprotected and to know you are not alone.

I trust this chapter will provide information, understanding, enlightenment and above all support in your coerced circumstances. You can begin by knowing another person's aggressive, manipulative and demeaning behaviour is nothing to do with you. **You did not cause their abusive behaviour**. Begin to develop self, know your employment rights and have a copy of your contract at hand. Your contract is your first safety document. Do not permit another employee to bully or intimidate you, or threaten your place at work. Assert boundaries, use assertive communication, recognise danger and deviousness rather than getting entangled in it.

It is rewarding and uplifting to work in a company that not only focuses on profit but regards its employee's wellbeing as a fundamental right. A company that provides training both for managers and employees. It has an education programme for *bullies, targets and bystanders.* It appoints qualified and designated resolution officer(s) who investigate and resolve any reported incidents of bullying behaviour. A company that **trains and encourages Upstander(s)** and train their Leaders to respect the dignity of each employee.

Culture of Safety & Wellness in the Workplace

A company's declaration with clear intention that workplace bullying is not tolerated and those who partake in it, will be addressed immediately. **Core Values include a code of conduct which exhibits high human consciousness of personal care standards.**

This message is pre-emptive and sets out to managers and other employees what is expected of them and how to align to the company's existing upstanding profile. The company's investment in human care standards, core values and the consciousness of human behaviour intelligence. A reputation that protects employees while still excel at being a global business leader.

Resolution Policy

A clear definition of what bullying behaviour is. The development of a conflict and resolution strategy, in line with the policy, which provides a method to address, resolve and stop workplace harassment. The company's policy will ensure that bullying causes the least amount of detriment on the company and its employees.

Resolution Group

A working group to identify, examine, and eradicate bullying and harassment. A staff support service that **is visible, responsive and proactive**. Key team leaders who appraise good working environments while addressing those areas lacking in their function and impact. If there is a report of bullying, a resolution officer(s) is available for dialogue immediately. The appointed person(s) is highly trained in the prevention, intervention and resolution of workplace bullying. A policy that works rather than an atmosphere of collusion and secrecy.

Programme to Empower Employees

A framework document that sets out steps of what to do if you feel your "safety" is being compromised. Once a target, makes contact with a resolution officer, it is imperative the employee is listened to and is provided with a safe place to confide in. The resolution officer will examine and record all details. The resolution officer cannot fob off the complainant and make comments like "toughen up" or "I found her/him alright". The resolution officer must clearly understand and relate to what the complainant is reporting. He/she will take this matter seriously and take the necessary qualified steps to resolve the crisis. The resolution policy will provide for an early assessment to cause less stress to the person making the grievance. Intervention must be provided immediately and a range of early resolutions, facilitated meetings, counselling, mentoring, and mediation as required. Any personal attack is seen as a serious illegal threat to a target's wellbeing in the workplace.

Reporting: Prevention & Intervention -

A supported safe place for managers, employees, bystanders who want to report bullying behaviour. Employers provide training that promotes the overall conduct of the company. **Employees are trained and have detailed procedures, guidelines and support to step up and speak up**. To know that there is a culture of non-acceptance of inappropriate behaviour.

Management are qualified to support and act when an employee confides in reporting bullying behaviour. If a bystander speaks up on behalf of a colleague there must a no-risk policy in place. The risk of not being believed, the risk of becoming the next target, the risk of ostracism. **THERE MUST BE NO RISK OF AVERSION OR AVOIDANCE.** There must a clear, open, designated and authentic system in place if bystander(s) are to feel safe making high involvement interventions. Risk aversion resolves nothing or does not stop perpetrators from perpetrating. There must be **CLEAR OPEN AND TRANSPARENT SUPPORT SYSTEM** in place. The reporting procedure is fair without fear of retribution or risks.

Addressing the Elephant in the Room

Once the perpetrator(s) of inappropriate behaviour is made aware, that his/her behaviour is being investigated, then the investigation may begin. If the perpetrator(s) agree that they have been at fault and agree to stop their inappropriate behaviour then both workers can resume their positions in the workplace. Usually, the behaviour is underhand coerced control, therefore, it is very difficult to actually pinpoint. Bullies are experts and form a pattern of manipulation, conspiracy, corruption and collusion. Bullies are experts at tactics that undermine the targets position. A bully must take ownership of their unhealthy behaviour and its effects on other employee(s). If they don't acknowledge their destructive impact, then there is a call for a psychological report before *or if* they can resume their position in their workplace.

The most productive resolution is management addressing the bullying behaviour immediately and requesting the perpetrator to stop. The perpetrator is informed that management is aware of their behaviour. An informal meeting with him/her but the message is clear and understood. Once the bully is aware that management are "actively aware", he/she will stop. Bullies know the atmosphere where nobody addresses their behavior and they can rule the roost without questioning. Mediation can be very powerful for restoring a healthy workplace.

Culture of Inspiration

Regular employee workshops create an atmosphere of accessible reliable support. A target will ask for help sooner rather than later. The perpetrator will know that this company does not tolerate bullying behaviour. A culture of peace and wellbeing will be more common than fear and oppression. A culture of new approaches for zero tolerance.

Intelligence is Consciousness of a Whole Human Being.

Intelligence is not merely academic intelligence, but includes a consciousness of a "whole human intelligence". Intelligence encompasses emotional, relationship, social, moral, physical and spiritual dimensions.

Academic Intelligence

Academic intelligence is but another area in the cognitive wheel to provide awareness for the **overall intelligence of a whole human being**. Often, high academic achievers are unconsciously aware that they lack certain other intelligences, e.g. social intelligence or emotional intelligence. They cannot comprehend how their academic education did not provide their wholeness. Society today, has placed so much emphasis on academic success than other intelligences.

Emotional Intelligence

Emotional Intelligence is the awareness of your personal emotional state. It is how you act, react and interact with others. EI is a gateway to understanding **your self-relationship and your role in a relationship with other(s) and with the world.** Emotional Intelligence is making healthy choices for personal growth and expansion. It is assertive thinking and actions in all environments and not being swayed by manipulation and threats.

Relationship Intelligence

How we see ourselves is greatly influenced by the people that we come into contact with during our journey through life. The development of "self" is dependent on those who are close or connected to us. Some of us may have had healthy supportive people, communities or societies, while others may have had abusive, neglectful or unhealthy. This affects how we see ourselves and on how we learn to interact safely or unsafely.

Bullies abuse power and have an obsession to desecrate your person, power, and reduce you until your "self" is non-existent and worthless. They want to destroy what is the essence of YOU.

Healthy relationships support YOU to reach your dreams, share your dreams and help you get back up when you are down. Healthy relationships want the best for **YOU**. Unfortunately for those who tolerate or inherit unhealthy relationships it manifests into **what is the worst for you, a loss of identity, pain, shame, isolation and fear**. A campaign to DESTROY YOU and your human presence on this earth.

TAKE CONTROL OF YOUR RELATIONSHIPS OR SOMEONE ELSE WILL. Unhealthy relationships will render you powerless. An unhealthy relationship will destroy your right to live a fearless, fulfilling and joyful life. It will be a life of struggle and conflict.

Spiritual Intelligence

Spirituality is a connection to our Higher Self and Higher Love and our Soul is a connection to Higher Power. It is the consciousness and awareness of our presence here on earth. Consciousness is the self-examination of where YOU are today. If our world is not serving us peace and love, then we must develop our awareness of consciousness.

We connect to spirituality and with self-examined, conscious people, find a place to grow in a safe place.

Social Intelligence

Is having self-awareness of one's own emotions while having the ability to understand, act, react and interact with other people's emotions and being part of social networks. It is the ability to recognize another person's emotional state, how it impacts on your emotional health, and knowing whether it is safe or unsafe.

Wellbeing & Safety- Vision, Strategy and Core Principles

I believe Leaders who have an open and fair policy, succeed. Treating and including all employees as equal contributing members of the team. Regular team meetings to liaise, listen and know what is happening on the ground. Employees who focus, process information, base it on facts and report it, in their designated areas. A workplace where gossip is not tolerated or approved. Inclusion and bringing people together, inspiring them to work and help each other on their career paths. A positive work culture that focuses on the well-being of the human. If someone has an aggressive communication pattern it must be addressed immediately as it really does create a fearful toxic atmosphere.

Poor management, non-resolution of conflict and a company without core-values is just a building without a heart. Most people respond and want to contribute their best if the company has healthy moral values. Today intelligent business leaders provide positive business models while also embracing the human side, a culture of wellbeing, safety and inclusion. A company that cares for its employees knows, its employees will in turn care for the company. Both sides are encouraged to be the best without harming each other's potential.

An Intelligent workplace understands the importance of Emotional, Social, Spiritual, Moral and Relationship Intelligence. An intelligent workplace provides a place of inspiration and personal development. Workplace Intelligence nurtures human potential and understands current employee climate. Intelligent Conscious Leaders can make the difference between a workplace culture of thriving or a culture of surviving in fear.

ABOUT THE AUTHOR

ERICA GIFFORD MILLS

Erica's favorite title, after that of Mom, is Coach. Erica admires and respects each person's decision to go on a journey of self-exploration to learn and grow personally and professionally as, she herself, is a lifelong learner. As a certified International Empowerment and Life Coach, she inspires, motivates and enlightens her clients to take a holistic and integrative approach to creating life balance, live a fulfilled life and love themselves fully. Erica's passion is to empower women and young ladies in taking that next step towards confidence, self-esteem building, boundary management, goal achievement and enabling them to feel and be heard.

Erica knows firsthand what it means to be in search of, find and create her balance and go after her passion with vigorous purpose. Spending 20+ years in the legal/compliance arena with government offices and corporations, Erica took the leap to go after what her heart and soul truly needed. She stopped doing what she was "supposed to do" and lives a life that sets her soul on fire. She remembers to live each day with passion, on purpose.

Erica equips her clients with tools and techniques to help them achieve success. She does this through individual coaching sessions, group coaching series (signature offering: *The Rooted Life ~ Live, Love, Let Go!*), women's retreats, workshops, speaking engagements, local and global volunteer efforts, as an author and as a talk radio host (***Get Rooted Radio ~ Living It Up, Loving It Up, Letting It Go***).

Contact:
Erica Gifford Mills
International Empowerment & Life Coach
Owner, Balanced Symmetree
Website: https://www.balancedsymmetree.com
Email: balancedsymmetree@gmail.com
Phone: +1 262.424.2548
Mailing Address: 5594 Arbutus Court, Greendale, WI 53129 United States
Facebook: https://www.facebook.com/eagiffordmills, https://www.facebook.com/BalancedSymmetree;
Instagram: https://instagram.com/BalancedSymmetree
Twitter: https://twitter.com/BalncdSymmetree
LinkedIn: https://www.linkedin.com/in/erica-mills-76403a7

TWENTY-THREE

Living with Passion, On Purpose

Erica Gifford Mills

"Be fearless in the pursuit of what sets your soul on fire."
—Jennifer Lee

This quote fuels me each day. It means understanding and acknowledging why I get out of bed each morning. And, believe me sometimes that is hard. Success is defined and measured in various ways. Depending on the individual, it might mean financial security, personal growth, professional development or creative expression. I believe finding something you are passionate about is the key to your success. Understanding what motivates you and makes your work fulfilling is essential to living with purpose. Taking action with passion is how you can live that life that sets your soul on fire.

There are many women out there in distress because they know they are meant for something immeasurable, but they don't know how to make it happen. They may not feel whole; like something is missing, not feeling like a total woman. I've been there; felt that. These women, longing for more, may be aching to leave the nine to five grind, or getting ahead in their career or climbing the corporate ladder, or just experiencing more joy, adventure and fulfilment in their life. If this sounds like you, this chapter is going to assist you in obtaining the clarity you're craving. You'll learn how to uncover your purpose, move forward with confidence and passion by creating a life you don't need a vacation from, and catapult you toward your greatest desires.

What is Life Purpose?

Some use terms such as finding your passion and finding your purpose interchangeably. I believe they are related and can rely on one another but are different. Every person has a life purpose. This isn't a fad; it is an international concept that has existed for ages. Most of us crave self-realization, and each of us needs to know that what we are doing makes sense. Otherwise, our own lives may not make sense to us. This happens at the intersection of passion and purpose. What is life purpose?

The Japanese call it 'Ikigai'. Combining the Japanese words 'iki', meaning life, and 'gai', meaning value or worth, Ikigai is then essentially about finding your purpose in life; a reason for being. The

French refer to purpose as 'raison d'être', also translated as a reason for being.

The Danish have a concept called 'Hygge'. There is not one word this can be translated into but the concept is so important the Happiness Research Institute in Copenhagen referred to it as part of the national DNA. It is a feeling of well-being, happiness and contentment through enjoying the simple things in life. In Hindu culture and yoga philosophy, you have 'Dharma'. Dharma means to support, hold or bear; often referred to as the path of rightness or the right way of living.

Great cultural lesson how does this help with uncovering your purpose? This shows that this life purpose concept is not new or unique and around the world we are searching for it. Even though life purpose is everywhere, purpose is personal and unique to the individual. All of the above concepts of life purpose center around what is at your core, your beliefs, and your values.

How do you uncover your life purpose and truly know your why? This is where you question *everything* and re-discover what truly is important to you now. What moves you? What inspires you? How well do you know yourself and what is truly at your core? You may be surprised to discover that your goals and intentions shift or deepen based on your higher understanding of the values that drive you. Here are ten techniques you can use to assist in uncovering your purpose and better knowing your why.

1. Explore the things you love to do

We are all born with a deep and meaningful purpose that we need to discover. Your purpose is not something you need to make up.

Begin by asking and answering yourself these two questions: what do you love to do; and, what comes easily to you? Then begin exploring those answers and be willing to try new things.

2. Expressing Qualities

What are two qualities you most enjoy expressing? Why? Now ask yourself, in what ways do I enjoy expressing these qualities? This is important because our behavior is defined by our underlying values, beliefs, convictions, and culture, to name just a few. Personal core values, consciously or subconsciously, are used as decision guidelines that keep you true to yourself and come out in your behavior and how you express yourself.

3. Conduct a Passion Test

Developed by Chris and Janet Attwood, the passion test is a simple technique. You start by filling in the blank 15 times for the following statement: *When my life is ideal, I am [blank].* Once you've created 15 statements, identify your top 5 choices and see where there are similarities. Next, create markers for each of your top 5 passions, so that you can easily tell whether you are living that passion. Once you know what your passions are and how your life will look when you are living it, you can create action plans to turn your dreams into reality (see # 9 on aligning goals).

4. Times You've Experienced Joy

Another technique you can use to help you identify your purpose is to conduct a joy review. Set aside time to make a list of all the times you've felt great joy in your life. List at least 10 and then look for a pattern among all these times. Joy is part of your internal guidance system telling you when you are on course (more on this in #7). You can determine and detect patterns about your life purpose from completing this joy review.

5. Fulfillment

Similar to the joy review, is the fulfillment test. Ask and answer the question: *when have I felt most fulfilled?* Then list a minimum of 10 times that you have felt fulfillment. What do your answers have in common? How do the answers correlate to the joy review? Are you beginning to see a pattern?

6. Create a Life Purpose Statement

Write a description of what the world would look like if it were operating perfectly according to you. *Life according to me [fill in the blank].* Think of it as your own mission statement. How would you feel? What would be different? The same? Now, combine this statement and the answers from questions 2 – 5 above into one statement, and you will have a better idea of your purpose. Be patient. This will take a little time. You may need to go through steps 1-6 a few times.

7. Follow Your Inner Guidance

What if I told you that you have your own guidance system within you that can help you get from where you are in life to where you want to go? For the system to work, it simply needs to know your beginning location and your end destination. All you have to do from that point on is follow the instructions it gives you to reach your destination.

Sounds so easy, right? But, you need to decide where you want to go; which can be the hard part. By clarifying your vision, then locking in your destination through goal setting, affirmations, and visualization, you will finally begin taking action that will move you in the right direction. That is following your inner guidance. It will take time, patience, continued effort and acceleration and some u-turns along the way. Once you clarify your life purpose statement and then stay focused on your vision, the exact steps will keep appearing along the way in the form of internal guidance, creating ideas, and new opportunities. Be open and ready to receive them.

8. Be Clear

Once you are clear about what you want and keep your mind constantly focused on it, the how will keep showing up—sometimes just when you need it and not a moment earlier. When you present your goals to the universe with all its powerful technology, you will be surprised and dazzled by what it delivers. This is where the magic and miracles truly happen.

Take some time to think honestly and openly about where you currently are in your life and what you want to do with your life. What is your financial status? How are your relationships? How is your health? Ask the tough questions and be truthful with yourself when answering.

Next, think about where you would like to be. If your life were perfect right now, what would it look like? How would you feel? What kind of job, hobbies, and/or adventures would you have and where would you be living? By continually doing this exercise, you'll send powerful triggers to your subconscious mind to help you get there.

9. Align Your Goals With Your Life Purpose and Passions

We're all gifted with a set of talents and interests that tell us what we're supposed to be doing. Once you know what your life purpose is, organize your actions and activities around it. Everything you do should be an expression of your purpose. If an activity or goal doesn't fit that formula, don't work on it. Aligning with your purpose is most critical when setting professional goals. When it comes to personal goals, you have more flexibility. Nurturing yourself mentally, emotionally, physically and spiritually will make you more energized, resilient and motivated to live your purpose.

Have you looked at your goals and how they are aligned with your life purpose statement? Are you working towards "things" that will get you where you need and want to be? Write down 3 goals that you have that will assist you in getting one step closer to living your passion-filled, purpose driven life.

10. Lean into Your True Life Purpose

Once you have gained more clarity about your purpose, you don't need to completely overhaul your life all at once. Instead, just lean into it, bit by bit. This is a marathon not a sprint. You must love yourself where you are and where you have been in order to move to where you want to be.

As mentioned throughout the 10 techniques, this isn't a one and done exercise. Some steps, if not all, will need to be repeated. You must remain focused, diligent and committed. Above all, you must be patient with yourself. Each step is movement in the right direction. Now that you are moving toward your purpose, how do you do it with passion?

Live with Passion

Follow your curiosity. Your curiosity just might lead you to your passion.
—Elizabeth Gilbert

True purpose is recognizing our own gifts and using them to contribute to the world. This is where we begin to live with passion. Be curious, connect with others and connect with yourself. This is your life and it's meant to be an exciting adventure; an exploration of your deepest self and, at times, the parts of yourself you didn't even know existed. Viewing your life, using a big picture view and allowing curiosity to creep in, can help you develop a better understanding of where you came from and where you'd like to go. It might bring out a whole new you and a whole different life. Be open to possible changes as there are times where we think we are destined to a path but another route opens. Allow yourself to be curious enough to check out that path.

We <u>must</u> live with passion. Passion is the vehicle that delivers us to purpose. Live as if you were to die tomorrow and continually learn as if you were to live forever. Embrace passion with reckless abandon; stop worrying about what could go wrong and lean into what could go right. Learning what makes you tick and knowing what allows you to use your gifts is something only you can do. But you need to do it on purpose. You need to be consistent, persistent and passionate.

Living with passion also means not letting others tell you what you should do. What I mean by this is not falling into the 'should of' trap. We have all had those moments. We do something or don't do something because we 'should'. We want to carry on the family tradition; or what we want to pursue may not be as secure of a job as another alternative. So we don't do what we really want but what we 'should'. Where your life path is headed may not be a cultural norm in your world; it may not be what your family wanted; it may not be what you originally sought out to do. BUT the best part of it is that it is _your_ decision!

Here are four tips to living with passion, on purpose:

1. Love what you do

Whether this is your job, career, volunteer effort, hobbies, do what you love and love what you do. As the old saying goes, "Do what you love and you'll never work a day in your life."

2. Build strong relationships

When we build healthier, stronger relationships with family, friends, and neighbors, we form our own army. Feeling loved and supported and giving that back in return, helps to find meaning in the inevitable hardships of life. Cherishing the relationships you have with loved ones allows you to live a life of passion. For this tribe is who will be there to root for you, celebrate with you and pick you up when times are tough. This is common sense but a reminder is necessary as building relationships is something that needs to be worked at and nurtured on a regular basis.

3. Gratitude

Being appreciative for the life you have; for the beauty around you and the lessons learned when times are hard, are all part of gratitude. The key is to be genuinely happy with what you have, and the universe will reward you with more in life. You'll start to live your life on your own terms and won't feel the need to compare yourself to others. Remember, comparison is the thief of joy. Our value and our achievements don't decrease in value just because someone else doesn't see them. We are being brought to things, discovering things and achieving things in our own time. Trust in that and carry gratitude in your heart.

4. Strive for progress

Strive for progress not perfection. Make a little movement, one step, every day towards your goals, dreams, towards the life that is burning to get out. As long as you keep trying and learning new things over time, you'll not only improve the quality of your life, but also discovering more out about yourself that you wouldn't find out otherwise.

People wait all week for Friday, all year for summer, and sometimes their whole life for the time to be right. You don't need to wait to create a life you don't need a vacation from. Once you realize this, you can start living your best life by creating it now. Be consistent, tenacious and confident on the path towards your dream of living a life that sets your soul on fire. Living with passion is a decision. You must make a conscious effort to do so.

Why are purpose and passion important and why are you stopping yourself?

"You are never too old to set another goal or to dream a new dream."
—C.S. Lewis

When it comes to the motivation to move forward and pursue your passion, a goal or a dream, nothing is more powerful than knowing it has meaning, it is your gift. It is the value contained within that allows you to engage with desire and diligence. No matter how successful we are, if we neglect what really matters to us, we will never be able to enjoy life to its fullest. When we neglect what matters must to us, this is where we feel incomplete, like something is missing. This is why passion and purpose are so important.

Purpose can guide life decisions, influence behavior, shape goals, offer a sense of direction and create meaning. As you maneuver through the steps above, as you begin living with passion, you might feel some fear and apprehension mixed with the excitement. Excitement is a fascinating and exhilarating part of the exploration. But also part of what holds you back.

Fear and limiting beliefs are what ends up stopping us. That little devil on your shoulder is whispering things like, *what if what matters most to me seems silly to others* or *what if I am rejected, laughed at, belittled? What if I fail? What if I succeed?* The thoughts, negative self-talk and doubts slide in.

This is when you must push past anxiety and self-doubt. You leap outside of your comfort zone, leap. You get comfy being uncomfy. Strength and growth happens when you are broken down, torn and pulled in other directions. No matter what happens, know that <u>fear is a liar</u>. It is a four letter word. Fear will make you second guess yourself; make up excuses and highlight all the reasons you shouldn't move forward.

But when you live with passion and live with a purpose, you will be infused with an element of grace in your life. Living with passion, on purpose, enables you to live a value-based life. For with purpose comes values, which are an integral aspect of one's life. Knowing your purpose allows you to live with integrity and as such it becomes easier to live a life that is true to your core values. When you are able to do this, you will feel gratified; as a person who knows their purpose tends to make a greater impact in the lives of others. When you commit to yourself, believe in yourself and allow yourself to lead with passion, amazing things will happen.

The process of uncovering your life purpose and doing it with passion has many benefits. Not only will you create a fulfilling new life for yourself but also become a more self-confident, evolved, positive and self-aware individual. Undertaking this journey of self-exploration, ultimately the search for your life purpose, may be the most central and satisfying adventure of your life. And this my beautifully empowered, total woman, is why we must live with passion, on purpose.

Dedication: To my siblings: Roberta, Chellie, Susan, Peggy, Harriett, Sandy, and Jerry, thank you. Being the baby has its advantages. We had two astounding role models in our parents who were true examples of *living with passion, on purpose.* But it was also through watching each of you, your lives and how you treat yourself and the women in your lives that I've learned being a Total Woman which has allowed me to *live with passion, on purpose.* I don't say it enough – THANK YOU. Love to you all.

ABOUT THE AUTHOR

Amicitia (Cita) Maloon-Gibson, PhD

Amicitia (Cita) Maloon- Gibson, Phd, is the Founder & President of MGAA Professional Development Institute and ATIC & MG Center for Excellence (non-profit). She has dedicated her career to develop others in a plethora of diverse industries. She is an expert advocate of selecting and developing talent for leadership and business success and has held various leadership roles in industries such as non-profit and for-profits on board of directors in corporation, ministries, state, local, Department of Defense and federal governments in the U.S. and international.

She is a retired Executive Leader with four decades of excellence in careers. She is a retired Army Lieutenant Colonel with 29 years of honorable and distinguished service to the nation with many Medals and Ribbons. She has worked in various leadership positions throughout Department of Defense with many distinguished civilian medals in the Federal Civilian Government. She was recently honor as Woman of Excellence and Woman Making a Difference in the Community. Her experiences are inclusive of local and national board of directors. A Professional Woman Network member for more than a decade and Advisory Board Member. She is a Certified John Maxwell Team Member; National Speakers Association Member and Power Woman, SHRM and Association of Training Development member to name a few.

Alumni of Webster University, Cornell University, Command and General Staff College and Federal Executive Institute. Her MISSION is Preparing the Next Generation of Leaders to Be Executives and the Best Leaders possible. She says, "Living is a part of giving and leaving a Legacy for the next Generation of Leaders." Additionally, she is a Servant Leader and founder of EWordSanctuary and outreach ministry helping others to thrive. Amicitia was ordained in 2005 by the late Bishop Thomas Solomon.

Contact:
P.O. Box 411482
Melbourne, Florida
(321) 537-5002
Email: maloon57@aol.com
Websites: www.Inspireleadgrow.com
www.EmpowermentDoc.com

TWENTY-FOUR

The Rise of the Total Woman: If Not Now, When? If Not You, Who?

Dr. Amicitia Maloon-Gibson

The year of Women on the Rise is Now for those reading this chapter.

There is no force more powerful than a woman determined and destined to rise to the next level of success in her career and relationships. Not too long ago it was not probable that a woman would have a "job" outside of the home. Perception in society and tradition was that a woman was to find a man, get married and have children.

Perhaps you can remember the slang, "A woman's purpose is to be barefoot, pregnant and submissive to her husband." Clergy at times use this "submissive" scripture out of context, as they forget to say, "as the husband submits to Christ." Well, not in today's society, as the socialization structure is clearly shifting. There is a "Shift in the Atmosphere and Growing Together" as a *family* is the new way of life.

Let me share a short historical perspective as it was in our mother's and grandmother's era in comparison with our society today, because family life is changing. Two-parent households are on the decline in the United States as divorce, remarriage and cohabitation are on the rise. And families are smaller now, both due to the growth of single-parent households and the drop in fertility. Not only are Americans having fewer children, but the circumstances surrounding parenthood have changed."

"While in the early 1960s babies typically arrived within the marriage, today fully four-in-ten births occur to women who are single or living with a non-marital partner. At the same time those family structures have transformed, so has the role of mothers in the workplace – and in the home. As more moms have entered the labor force, more have become breadwinners – in many cases, *primary* breadwinners – in their families." (Source: National Vital Statistics Report Volume 48, Number 16.)

As a result of these changes, there is no longer one dominant family form in the U.S. as parents today are raising their children against a backdrop of increasingly diverse and, for many, constantly evolving family forms. By contrast, in 1960, the height of the post-World War II baby boom, there was one dominant family form. At that time 73% of all children were living in a family with two married parents in their first marriage. By 1980, 61% of children were living in this type of family, and today less than half (46%) are. The declining share of children living in what is often deemed a "traditional" family has been largely supplanted by the rising shares of children living with single or cohabiting parents.

Not only has the diversity in family living arrangements increased since the early 1960s, but so has the fluidity of the family. Non-marital co-habitation and divorce, along with the prevalence of remarriage and (non-marital) recoupling in the U.S., make for family structures that in many cases continue to evolve throughout a child's life. While in the past a child born to a married couple – as most children were – was very likely to grow up in a home with those two parents, this is much less common today, as a child's living arrangement changes with each adjustment in the relationship status of their parents. For example, one study found that over a three-year period, about three-in-ten (31%) children younger than 6 had experienced a major change in their family or household structure, in the form of parental divorce, separation, marriage, cohabitation or death.

(Source: The American Family Today, PEW Research Center Washington D.C. (Parenting in America, December 17, 2015 (pewsocialtrends.org)

**Data chart from PWE Research Center (used with permission from public records.)

Now is your time to rise to the top! A significant shift in the environment is taking place. This is indicative by the results in the 2018 Elections of Women in Political Leadership roles in a historical grand-slam! Shifting of leadership positions traditionally held by males, specifically White males are being filled by women of all cultural ethnicities. Glass ceilings are being broken in corporate America and among the Military Armed. Forces. Also, women are getting more involved in politics in positions of Mayor, Senator and Governor.

Many women who held hourly positions are shifting to salary positions. As I reflect back on my life in various positions that I filled, I was the first (woman) or the only (African American) including appointments on boards of directors. I was happy to be there and have the position or seat at the table. However, my gut feelings was to be quiet and say nothing unless I was asked to speak. Now, I make it a point to accept positions on boards where my voice will not be muted. So, I say to you women on the rise, get the seat at the table or the position at the top and use your voice to impact positive change. Fear not, and you can enter the doors of opportunities as you elevate. Now is your time to rise, if not now when? If not you, then who?

"Diversity and Inclusion is about connection and commitment. Can we commit to getting along and communicate to learn more about similarities and less about differences." —Dr. Amicitia Maloon-Gibson

You have the ability to change lives long after you transition from this world. On your way up here on earth, take at least two with you. As you rise ask yourself, how do you want to be remembered (Legacy)? Now as you rise, if you don't like the hand you are dealt, change the end of your story.

Do this by repositioning yourself with new Goals and Objectives that are Measureable to propel you on journey from best to better.

We all have a personal Truth in our lives as what we will or will not accept as we Rise to the Top in our lives. This should include the positive, negative and ugly aspect of our lives called lessons learned (mistakes). Only you can determine what your "Truth" is as you become the real you as a leader. Here are a few assessment steps that may help you.

Why? Because the higher you elevate as a "Total Woman On The Rise," the more you are under a microscope and criticized as a public figure. The blank spaces are for you to write your "Truth" or make necessary adjustments to be better and the best you.

Self-Assessment for your Truth

Look at the person in the mirror: Do a self-assessment about a choice you have made knowing you could have made a more positive decision. Get feedback from valued mentors and peers. Address the issue and ask yourself what you should have done differently. Take corrective actions. Be that role model for others to follow as you own your mistakes or challenges.

_____

_____

_____

Return to work in or outside the home: Preparation and planning empowers a system for moving forward versus marching time (staying in the same space) and doing nothing.

_____

_____

_____

Together with your team (work/family) have a conversation on issues: Getting feedback for those surrounding you gives you more accuracy on a resolution for the challengers (strengths/weaknesses).

The strengths will become stronger and the weakness can merge as strengths

_____

_____

_____

Collaboration with others staffers/executives helps put ambiguity into perspective and a clearer vision of ownership of responsibilities: Ask them how you can help them and communicate how they can help you. Together you can Rise as a Team.

_____

_____

_____

"Great leadership is not a solo act. It's a group performance. You need to connect through the heart to lead effectively." —Robert Vanourek

Many have written on the subject of leadership and come to the conclusion that great leaders are born and not made, but we know that's not correct.

However, with the right attitude, education, dedication to working hard and persistence, you too can become a great leader. Here are some Stepping Stones to Success that will help you move to your next level in any career. Women on the Rise are most likely to be results- driven, goal-oriented and prepared.

1. **You must be hungry:** Some call it Passion or Desire. At the forefront is your desire to lead. Check yourself – is this what you are here on this earth to do? Leadership takes a great deal of work, so identify what motivates you. Identify what you most want to achieve in your life and the life of others.

   Ralph Waldo Emerson said and I quote "Nothing great is ever achieved without passion."

2. **You must see clearly the End of Your Story:** Where you want to be and a timeline with action plans. This is call Vision. It is the difference you want to make in your community as an individual or part of a team. As a member of the Baby Boomer Era, I personally can envision a legacy, leaving something for the next generations, making giving a part of living. Ask yourself, what are you created to do or why were you called to do _____ (fill in the blank).

3. **Creativity is where your plan begins:** This stage is where you seek feedback from your mentors and family support for help and recommendations on the ideas you have generated. Sometimes you will have to encourage yourself, as it gets lonely as you Rise to the Top.

   John Quincy Adams said, "If your actions inspire others to dream more, learn more, do more and become more, you are a leader."

4. **Get Certifications in your area of Expertise:** Associations and professional organizations are where you can acquire additional knowledge, skills and abilities. Become a student for life. Empower yourself in your area and be the best from the inside out. Reposition

helps you to be flexible in positions and diverse environments. As a lead, you are being watched. Be a self-disciplined, confident a team-builder and decisive. Be the one others can Trust in a critical moment.

5. **Respect:** Respect for others is an essential attribute in a woman on the Rise as a great leader. You should help others (especially women) celebrate their achievements and accomplishments. Jealousy and hatred will not generate respect and will diminish your power as a leader. The late Aretha Franklin, sang about Respect in one of her number one record hits.

   "A leader take people where they want to go. A great leader *takes people where they don't necessarily want to go, but ought to be."* —Rosalynn Cart

6. **Your Health is your Wealth:** Broken and bleeding leaders can't serve well. Be physically and mentally fit and connect to a higher source. Put **God First** in all you do and your dreams will be fulfilled in due season. I believe that season is now! Now is your time to Rise! Rise up, speak up and stand up "Total Woman" on the Rise.

Notes:

ABOUT THE AUTHOR

KATHIE BRITTON

Kathie Britton is a proud mother of two young adults, Matthew age 22 and Grace age 20. Kathie loves to spend time with family and friends in the outdoors, whether it be hiking or camping in the beautiful settings of northern Canada. Kathie has shared her love of traveling with her children, exploring coast to coast across Canada and beyond.

She is a member of a hospital Senior Leadership team in the role of planning, service quality, and integration. Kathie has centre on leadership roles within primary and acute care settings, focusing on team development, change management, and health system redesign. She holds a Master of Health Leadership, Bachelor of Arts and Bachelor Science undergrad degrees. Her current focus is on completing her Master of Business from Heriot-Watt Edinburgh Business School.

TWENTY-FIVE

Lessons for Our Daughters

Katherine Britton

"To my beautiful daughter, always remember you are brave, you are capable, you are pretty, and you can accomplish ANYTHING your heart desires! I know this because I am your Mother." —Author Unknown

Being a mother is the most precious gift ever provided by our creator. I am a mother of two beautiful children, now young adults, Matthew and Grace. As much as I will focus on lessons for our daughters, I would encourage men to read and understand the importance of raising a strong, capable, and courageous woman. This will transpose to future relationships between a man and a woman and how they manage the world we share. How we raise our daughters have significantly changed over the years. While the lessons we may have provide decades or centuries back focused on a women's role within a family unit and community, we now teach our daughters to consider themselves in many different environments and their ability to achieve anything they desire. I understand and respect that culture and beliefs differ across our world, I will focus on the lessons that my family has passed down for generations. Nelson Mandela said, "you can start changing our world for the better daily, no matter how small the action." Our daughters will chart their course in life according to what we share and teach them, we have the gift of encouraging a life filled with strength, power, beauty, and joyfulness. This is not necessarily a chapter on a mother's lesson for daughters as that would be disrespectful to the men that are taking a strong role in raising their children. This is chapter is for mothers, fathers, family, and friends that are raising our next generation of strong, capable women. In the pages to come, there are ten lessons for our daughters, and I encourage to consider how it could apply to you and your family. My daughter has taught me more about myself then I could have ever imagined and for that I am truly grateful for as much as these are lessons for our daughters, they are also for the parents raising the next generation.

Be Strong and Brave

"What I wanted most for my daughter was that she be able to soar confidently in her own sky, where ever that might be, and if there is space for me as well, I would, indeed, have reaped what I had tried to sow"
—Helen Claes

Our daughters will learn from our past, do not be afraid to share with them the best and hardest parts of your world. You are the teacher, mentor, and coach and will prepare your daughter for the challenges she will face. Daughters, our greatest wish for you is to be the strong, powerful woman you are. Have the courage to live your life with passion and determination. Express yourself with your own thoughts and opinions, never allowing others to dominate your actions or beliefs. Live your life bravely and never with fear. Fear will wear you down, leaving you hollow and empty. Reach deep within your soul and be the strong and brave individual you were meant to be. You are truly a warrior and is meant to lead your life with resolution and purpose.

> **Ten Lessons for our Daughters**
> Be strong and brave
> Joy comes from living with a giving soul
> Live with patience, forgiveness, and compassion
> Be adventurous and curious about the world we share
> Live with independence
> Honour yourself with self-respect and self-love
> Be the beautiful person you are
> Leave room for your happiness
> Build a bridge over the bad days and mistakes
> Be thankful for all you are and all you have

Be the beautiful person you are

"True beauty in a woman is reflected in her soul" —Audrey Hepburn

Mothers remember what Berne Brown stated, "I can encourage my daughter to love her body, but what really matters are the observations she makes about my relationship with my own body." Remember they will see themselves through our eyes and their own as well. Our daughters will teach us in the behaviours that they model after us for they are truly a reflection of ourselves. Daughters have a healthy relationship with your own bodies, beauty is not what you see on the outside, it starts within your soul. Learn to love every part of your body including what is reflected in the mirror. Love yourself for the beautiful soul that you are and radiate that for others to see. Be yourself and if that means dancing in the rain or wearing a pink flowing dress then by all means, you be you. Beauty is truly reflected in a woman who can laugh, dance, and share her soul with others in a giving and loving way. This is the essence of beauty.

Joy comes from living with a giving soul

"One thing that I ask you: Never be afraid of giving. There is a deep joy in giving, since what we receive is much more than what we give"
—Mother Teresa

Giving from deep within yourself, with no expectation of return, you will receive tremendously more. Everyday strive to do one thing for another human, animal, or our planet we share, and the joy will naturally flow. There is great opportunity every day to make a difference is someone else's life that we should ensure we are reflecting this in our own lives for the sake of teaching our daughters this worthy lesson. The small acts of kindness matter and gives just as much back to our own souls. Daughters give with enthusiasm, joy, and happiness that comes from deep within and do not be afraid to reflect that on to others. Do it everyday with purpose and commitment and you will witness the beauty of a selfless giving heart and experience the joy it can bring to yourself and others.

Live with patience, forgiveness, and compassion

"Did I offer peace today? Did I bring a smile to someone's face? Did I say words of healing? Did I let go of my anger and resentment? Did I forgive? Did I love? These are the real questions." —Henri Nouwen

To be able to live a life with peace and love, it starts first with patience, forgiveness, and compassion for ourselves. For how can we show others if we can not find it within our self to be accepting of our own being. By letting go of behaviours that hurt us we take away another's ability to continue to damage our well-being. No greater gift of empathy, kindness and tolerance could be taught to our Daughters, well we should not allow people to continually to behave in a manner that hurts, the ability to rise above and create boundaries is critical for personal growth. Speak only with kindness and love, no small act will go unnoticed by those around you. Root yourself with the ability to consider others and how they might be suffering or struggling. Empathy should be given freely with no judgement towards others. As we move towards living a life with patience, compassion, and forgiveness we can come to a place of peace and gentleness for others and ourselves.

Be adventurous and curious about the world we share

*"We keep moving forward, opening new doors, and doing new things,
because we're curious and curiosity keeps leading us down new paths"*
—Walt Disney

What better lesson could we teach our daughters then to live life with adventure and curiosity. Share your stories, relive your dreams through the eyes of your daughters, create new experiences, and let it all take life in their dreams. Take unscheduled times to explore your surroundings close and far away. It never needs to be complicated or expensive, a simple opportunity to even explore your own neighbourhood or community can create the excitement of adventure and curiosity. Ask the questions of why or what or when, create an opportunity for critical thinking and exploration. Listen to your daughters tell stories of the adventures and what they have learned and experienced. Audrey Hepburn stated, "Noting is impossible, the word itself says I'M possible." My Mother was the best teacher for reinforcing that impossible is not a permitted word in the family and we should seek out what we do not know and experience all we could.

Live with purpose and independence

*"You'll learn, as you get older, that rules are made to be broken. Be bold
enough to live life on your terms, and never, ever apologize for it. Go
against the grain, refuse to conform, take the road less traveled instead of
the well-beaten path. Laugh in the face of adversity and leap before you
look. Dance as though everybody is watching. March to the beat of your
own drummer. And stubbornly refuse to fit in."* —Mandy Hale

Live your life with purpose and independence, *"start embracing the life that is calling you, find your calling, know what sparks the light in you so you – in your own way – can illuminate the world." Oprah Winfrey* Your life journey can only be defined by you and how you choose to react to the situations you find yourself in. Be fiercely independent and commit to your dreams with action and purpose. Use opportunities of silence to find yourself and the answers you are seeking. Learn to look inside yourself for the strength to live independently and with a strong conviction to living the life you were meant to live.

Honour yourself with self-respect and self-love

"You yourself, as much as anybody in the entire universe, deserve your love and affection." —Buddha

My son at age three informed his teacher that "this school does not respect my individuality!". Precious words that could never be truer. We need to start by celebrating and respecting our own individuality for self-love is so important for our growth and well-being. For how can we teach our daughters to love others if they can not first love themselves? It is critical that we support our daughters to live with confidence and not self-judgement or judgment from those around them. If there is one lesson, we can share with our beautiful daughters is to love themselves enough that they will never permit emotional, physical, or sexual abuse from anyone in their life. The scars and trauma are personal to each woman and long in healing and life altering. From all the lessons we need to pass on to our daughters it is to have the strength to set boundaries in relationships and not permit a partner to dictate how another person is to think, believe, or behave. Abuse in any form should not be permitted and silence does not make it stop or go away. There is no easy solution except to start with self-love and self-respect as a foundational lesson. Let's all agree to teach our children to find their own inner beauty and self-worth for they will and always should feel like they "are enough in this universe" notesonbliss.com.

Leave room for your happiness

"The best music I have ever heard is the sound of my daughter's giggling"
—Debasish Mridha

Simply, live with joy and happiness. This may seem like an easy task however it does take effort. Living life with happiness can be a choice that is made daily. Abraham Lincoln, stated that "most people are about as happy as they make their minds to be." It is the simple joys in life that can bring true happiness to our world. Face each day with the desire and choice to greet the day with positivity, cheerfulness, and an excitement for life. Life does not need to be so series, laugh out loud and live happily in the moment.

Build a bridge over the bad days and mistakes

"Isn't it nice to think that tomorrow is a new day with no mistakes in it"
—Lucy Maud Montgomery, Anne of Green Gables

Lucy Maud Montgomery was an author who told the tale of a young red headed orphan girl who lived on Price Edward Island,

Canada. This young girl has the resilience to live her life with a positive attitude and the belief that tomorrow was always a new day with no mistakes. An important gift to pass on to our daughters is that each day is an opportunity for change and to start anew at dawn with a wonderful, beautiful day with the rise of the sun. Living a life that is focused on negativity and pessimism can only lead to sadness and resentment. My dearest friend Brenda McGuire always said, "build a bridge and get over it". Her words of wisdom have led me to strive to live with a positive attitude, letting go of past hurts and mistakes. A wish for the next generation of daughters is to focus on the blessings of their life rather then the "potholes" we can find ourselves in from time to time. We all need to reflect on past actions and then accept or change for our next experiences.

Be thankful for all you are and all you have

"Choosing to be positive and having a grateful attitude is going to determine how you're going to live your life." —Joel Osteen

With the dawn of each day we truly have the opportunity to be thankful that our eyes open, our feet can touch the ground, and we can express our gratitude for the quiet beauty of a sunrise. Build your life around focusing, with gratitude, on the foundational building blocks of your world including your health, relationships, and home. Teach and model for your daughter the ability to recognize that they create their world with the attitudes and opinions. The words they choose to speak or think will create a negative or positive environment. To our daughters, be aware of the beauty that surrounds you, the birds that sing, the clouds that dance across the sky, the friends that hold your hand when you are laughing or crying, and the arms that hold you in love while you fall asleep. Determine your life today, be thankful for your blessings.

One final word on lessons for our Daughters

Dr. Seuss sums up our final thoughts for our daughters. Encourage your daughters to express themselves with all their might and be true to themselves for there will never be someone just quite the same. They are beautiful in their own unique and precious way and it is not our role to change our children but engage with them as they grow and mature into adult

hood. What a blessing from our creator, to be trusted with the most precious being of all, our children.

What are your lessons for our daughters? What legacy will you share with your daughter? How would this shape how you raise a son to one day perhaps marry and have daughters of his own? Consider your thoughts here....

_____

_____

_____

_____

_____

_____

_____

_____

What is your journey that you would share with your daughter? Take your time to reflect on the importance of your life and the milestones you have travelled.

_____

_____

_____

_____

_____

_____

_____

_____

Written with love for my beautiful daughter Grace and son Matthew. I am humbled to be their Mother and forever grateful for the lessons they have taught me about how to love, laugh, and lively simply in the moment.

ABOUT THE AUTHOR

SONY AVRITT STEIER

Sony Avritt Steier is the past and current chair of Light the Night with the Leukemia and Lymphoma Society. She and her family have been personally impacted by the disease when she lost her best friend and sister Tina. Her primary civic an philanthropic passion is to eradicate Leukemia and Lymphoma through research funding where she serves on the local chapter's board. Sony is president and operating partner of Steier Properties, a diverse real estate portfolio of multi-family housing that includes condos, developments, single family homes and vacation rentals. She has a BS in Business Administration from Sullivan University and is an alumni of Delta Zeta Sorority. Sony and her husband Joe support varies charities, civic organizations and numerous academic institutions throughout the city including Bellarmine University, Kids Cancer Alliance, Hand In Hand, the Parklands and was co-chair of the Sacred Heart Academy Interlude. Sony is the proud mother of four children: Joseph, Jacqueline, Luke and Ava.

TWENTY-SIX

Finding Purpose and Passion

Sony Steier

"There is a lot of good in your life- don't take it for granted. Don't get focused on the struggles that you miss the gift of today." —Joel Osteen

Like many of you in our great quest for finding the elusive happiness, I've searched externally looking for the perfect self-help guide fo improving my self- esteem and confidence. I have a whole shelf of them. There's such a vast collection in helping us to improve, being our best selves, saying "yes", gratitude journals, positive thinking, and being the "best me" books to advise us on what it takes. I've watched late night infomercials and clicked on advertisement earning me more exercise gimmicks than I could count. The Brazilian Butt and South Beach Body videos did not give me either one. You name it, I've tried it. I know I'm not alone as I peruse the aisles of my favorite book store. Would happiness come from a better physique or the newest fashion? There are so many options for improvement, yet I never took the time to simply put time in and explore the real me.

So many women want to find "happiness" and are often being let down by a lack of it. Some need anti-anxiety meds to quiet the voice that says we are not good enough. Working moms face the pressures of achieving with the guilt of juggling motherhood yet feeling like they are failing at both. Stay- at- home moms have different pressure for social approval with their choice, knowing experts say it's a win for children to have a parent home full- time, but studies show they feel higher levels of sadness and isolation according to Gallup polls. When the universe sends us signs, do we listen? When we get older, our default says I can't do this because I'm not good at it. It's ok to try and fail but never challenging ourselves is the tragedy. What does happiness even look like for women? In deep reflection, I've explored my own journey and have pinpointed 5 areas that have directed me toward a deeper more fulfilled life and the mistakes I've encountered along the way.

Love and Coupling

When I met my husband Joe, I was 19 years old. I was young and attractive yet secretly insecure. I was looking to find the worst in men so when they did not meet my expectations, I was quick to walk away. When there was an argument, I resorted to raising my voice and often hurling the closest movable object across the room. One day, after breaking one of Joe's sculptures, he looked at me and said, "I love you, but I don't want to have this kind of life." It hit me hard realizing my anger was not a fiery suggestion of love, but a real problem if I wanted to have this quality man in my life. From that point, I can't say I never threw anything, but I knew I had to change my tactics in order to find the peace and control every relationship should strive to have.

A relationship has two people with entirely different life experiences. Our fundamental beliefs are instilled within us. The way we perceive a conversation, intention and action can be a hit or a disaster. On social media, it looks like certain couples are perfect with their adventures and selfies cheek to cheek. I am guilty of posting this image as well. It is much more fun posting the good times than the bad. Yet, marriage is full of both. Each relationship has seasons.

According to Gary Chapman, a renown marriage counselor, "My experience, both in my own marriage and in counseling couples for more than 30 years, suggests that marriages are perpetually in a state of transition, continually moving from one season to another-perhaps not annually, as in nature, but just as certainly and consistently. The cycle repeats itself many times throughout the life of a marriage." Fall and winter are the more challenge periods where you are not connecting and feeling bitter and cold. Some action must be done to improve the relationship when it feels this way, or it may wither. Not all is bad with this season, as sometimes it takes a wake-up call to stimulate growth. Chapman has found, "all couples face difficulties, and all couples have differences. The real problem is when couples fail to negotiate these differences. "

I've had this wake-up call. You either improve or are doomed for failure. The biggest point of contention for us has been parenting our children, and feeling the other person is lacking in support. At some point, we had to realize we can not change our partner in their fundamental beliefs and parenting style. You will not always agree on finances, how to discipline the kids, and may have huge personality differences at times, but if you are having the same battle repeatedly, you must come up with a treaty. Otherwise, the conversation turns into counterpoints and ends up causing more damage than resolution. Discuss your family plan and goals when you are calm, then look back to what was decided and follow that goal. Make having the spring and summer seasons in your relationship the norm.

I have learned I cannot let things fester inside of me. If I have something to say, I have to discuss it in a reasonable amount of time. I try the approach, "You may not have realized this, but when you did this, I felt this way," without accusation. Sometimes we still disagree on what the intention was, but generally your partner cannot get angry when you approach it with sincerity. I have noticed the more stress and pressure at work, the less impartial he is on perceived criticism. In that case, it's something I take into account to be discussed at a better time. When he is down and unhappy, I want to be the positive partner. When I am, he does the same for me. We have learned to be receptive to each other's needs. We grow stronger as a couple with this type of communication and in supporting each other's needs.

Another action that has worked for us: Always Date your Mate. It is easy to fall into the perpetual state of comfort, loose clothing and no make up, especially when you work from home.

Yet, at the very minimum once a month, dress nicely, make yourself look good and fire up your sparkling sense of humor and adventurous side. Even if Joe and I can't go out until 9pm, we have our date night. Kids will always have sports, their homework, and a house that needs to be cleaned, but put it on hold. Your children will see you put effort into each other, and they will get a feeling of security seeing their parents loving one another. Don't invite other friends, just focus on one another. Compliments are encouraged. I was watching a comedy recently, and one character mentions to another stressed-out husband, "try telling your wife two compliments each day. One, tell her something positive about her physical self. Include words like beautiful, sexy, amazing. Second, tell her a compliment about what she does that you appreciate." Who knew a comedy has so much wisdom in it? I noticed Joe does this for me and has for years, and it has built my confidence and trust. When our kids were younger, this was our time. I needed it desperately. It is normal to feel frustrated at your partner and all the little things they didn't do correctly. A glass of wine and connecting face to face with your partner is critical and worth the energy it takes. Most of the time, we are more focused on our children than our partners, so let this be a time to put each other first.

First there were Two, then Three, Four, Five and Six

After having Joseph, then Jacqueline 3 years later, followed by Luke 2 years after and finishing with Ava 18 months, I felt like a baby- making machine. I was a constant caregiver, busy with diapers, feedings and baths. Though these are beautiful years that I would never change, it took a lot out out of me. If you asked me my hobbies, I'd have to wonder if keeping kids alive and fed would be a good answer. Some men really enjoy the baby phase. I don't think that was Joe until a bit later. He still worked 80 hours a week and luckily, I had help with an au pair program. When my third child Luke came, he was born at 28 weeks and due to a questionable OBGYN, he was not prepared. I had an emergency C-Section at an emergency room, and Luke fought for his life at birth. He had respiratory distress and was on a ventilator.

Luke had hydrocephalus and a level 4 intraventricular hemorrhage (a brain bleed). This was a very difficult period in our lives topped with the fact we were not in our hometown when this happened but fleeing a Florida hurricane. I stayed at the Ronald McDonald House in Ft Myers, Florida by Luke's side. Everyday was a rollar coaster knowing up to a third of babies with this type of bleed may not survive. I was told this condition may affect his mental and physical capacities for life and surely, he would have damage. Hearing your baby may never walk or talk was a devastating blow to both Joe and me, but we knew we would love Luke no matter the outcome. Luke did survive, and he has fought hard for all his capabilities with every kind of therapy known and medical specialists' visits for many years. When two people go through an experience like this, it either bonds you together or tears you apart. Both of us took the blessing of Luke's life and made it count. He has inspired our family and others that know him, and continues to grow and succeed.

Each of our children have had their special challenges. None so dramatic as Luke, but with diagnosis of learning differences, ADHD, dyslexia, middle school drama, and bullies. There are so many minefields that kids can go through today. The nights I have spent sleepless in bed worrying are countless. Yet, in the end, you just believe in your kids, assure them they are loved and are amazing. Never judge or compare them to others especially in front of them. Find their special talent or gift and encourage it. If they don't feel you are proud of them 100%, they quit believing in themselves. Find laughter in bad times. We have learned to do the best we can and believe that they will get through adversity with the values and reassurance we have instilled.

Create lasting memories with your children. It can be as simple as taking them to the park and walking trails, allowing a pet or two, creating an adventure in the everyday and having good conversations treating them like they are important. Magic for children comes in all forms. One of my best memories was attending a wedding in Europe with Luke and Ava. I knew my two oldest children in high couldn't miss, but Luke and Ava were in middle school. Would they miss lessons? Yes, but they are not vying for colleges just yet. We got on a plane just the three of us and headed to Sweden where Luke was the best man, and Ava was reading a poem for our former au pair Mattias and his wife Ida. Ava practiced her Swedish, and Luke prepared his speech. It was a magical day. Since we were there, we thought we might as well go to Denmark.

This trip sparked such adventure and imagination in them, the kind of education you can't learn in school. Sometimes you just say "yes!"

Value in Friendships

When I moved back to Louisville from South Florida, I learned a very important lesson in Life. Women need friendships. We need to connect in honest ways that only women understand. I had play dates with other moms but there is something critical about finding the trust and love in other women. We are made differently than males and connect in confiding and listening. I was embraced by a group of women who I adore. I was very guarded at times after being hurt with friendships, but I have learned when people show you who they are, believe them. I've also seen women that encourage, support and love one another. When I have needed them, they have come through again and again. Allow yourself to open up to women and develop that bond. Each relationship is not the same; they have their own special quality that connects us. Without these friendships, I know my cup would not be full. I have learned you get what you give, so it takes love and effort to grow a relationship. I took my first ever girls' trip, and we were as silly as can be. Rarely had I laughed that hard and still enjoyed meaningful conversations. When I returned, I was a new woman ready to take on the world. We need that support from our family and friends allowing us to take a break. My husband supports this 100% because he wants to see me happy, and I always appreciate the effort he puts forth so I can go. For any woman, a break from the chaos of life is a welcome retreat. Even if it is one night away, make that time to enjoy yourself.

Random Acts of Kindness Opens your Heart

I am far from perfect but am committed to making this world a better place when I leave it. While driving with my daughter Jacqueline, we saw an older man in a wheelchair struggling to cross the road at a red light. I got out to help, and realized he was a homeless man who was looking ill. He needed help and was hungry. With a slight hesitation, I loaded his wheelchair and we drove to the nearest Burger King. Everyone stared. His name was Ivan. He was exhausted, dehydrated and needed a bath. I offered to take him home to bathe and rest, but I did check his bags for safety. As soon as we pulled in, his stomach started to retch. I got him to the bathroom just in time, then he fell asleep immediately. He could not lie down flat since he had been upright for so long. I called my husband and said, "Don't be mad at me but I brought a homeless man home," and I explained. When he awoke, he was unbearably itchy. I took him to the outside shower to make it easier to bathe him. I peeled off his socks, and he had the worst infection. His skin was deeply covered with white holes that looked so painful. He had no toes just a wide club foot. I cleaned his wounds and hid my discomfort. Washing his hair and back, he moaned at not having had human touch. After he was changed, he looked so clean and happy. While he had slept, I called around trying to find a place for him to stay. From his story he was a vet, but they did not have any record of him. I found a men's shelter, but when I mentioned this option, he said he would not be locked up at night and would not go there or to the hospital. I remembered, Joe's father who had been diagnosed with pancreatic cancer, had been with us visiting, and we had a new wheelchair at our home during his stay. I was able to switch Ivan's damaged wheelchair for the brand new one. What are the chances I just happened to have this at my house? Ivan was ready to go, but first wanted me to find him his favorite cigar called Zanzibar's.

There was a store not far away. Afterwards, I took him to where he wanted to be dropped off, gave him money and his washed clothes in a bag, and we said goodbye. As I turned around, he was sitting in his new wheelchair, smiling and lighting up the Zanzibar. My daughter still talks about Ivan and says a prayer he is ok somewhere. A random act of kindness is a gift to yourself and makes us all feel human.

Finding Purpose and Passion

Too often we say we are not good at something. Usually it makes us feel uncomfortable, and we don't want to try. I've always said I am bad at public speaking. An invitation came to help a cause so very close to my heart. I was asked to chair Light the Night with the Leukemia and Lymphoma Society; a beautiful fundraising walk each year. My initial response was "I don't think I can do it." It would entail asking businesses to sponsor, forming team, talking to groups, interviews and speaking to a large crowd of over 1,000 on the night of the event. Every part of me said "absolutely not!" I thought about my sister's journey.

Tina was my older sister and best friend. She was 29 years old and 21 weeks pregnant when she was diagnosed with Acute Lymphoblastic Leukemia. She battled this painful blood cancer, and sadly lost her baby shortly after being diagnosed. She turned 30 with a surprise party with all of her friends and family.

Nine months later, while preparing for a bone marrow transplant, she caught pneumonia and died at age 30. She had to face the fear of death, losing her child and the physical pain of chemo and radiation. She had more courage in her journey than any person I've known. Tina would have told me to stop being afraid and think of what I was doing this for.

I reluctantly said "yes." The whole experience in helping raise money for research, treatments, education and patient support changed my life. I opened a piece of my heart that was damaged and let hope back in. Hearing the stories of those touched by cancer changed me to the core. I stood on that stage that night, and I looked over the crowd including my mother and brother. Each person was holding a lantern red (for support), gold (in memory) and white (the survivors), and I knew I found a true passion. I could not save Tina, but together we can fight to save all the people suffering blood cancer now. I remember Tina saying after one particularly grueling treatment with tears in her eyes, "I can't imagine a child going through this." Leukemia is the #1 children's cancer. The positive is there has been more advancements in the last 5 years than in the previous 40, and treatments made for blood cancers frequently become used for many of the other cancers. Since this experience, not a day that has gone by where I feel sorry for myself or don't feel thankful for life. I live with gratitude and want to honor my sister and the many people fighting cancer. Purpose is something we all need in life.

"Do every act of your life as though it were the last act of your life."
—Marcus Aurelius

ABOUT THE AUTHOR

YOLANDA Y. MCINTOSH

Yolanda Y. McIntosh is the Corporate Equal Employment Opportunity (EEO) Officer for a large heavy/highway construction company in Minnesota. Her primary responsibilities include ensuring all employment practices and workplace environments are free of discrimination and harassment. Ms. McIntosh is responsible for identifying, investigating and resolving discrimination complaints and is responsible to assist in the implementation of remedial action to meet compliance requirements and goals. Ms. McIntosh also acts as a liaison between the company and other relevant community and governmental enforcement agencies and organizations as necessary. In addition, Ms. McIntosh coordinates employee and company support of community based programs that may lead to full employment of women, people of color, and people with disabilities. As a frequently sought after industry guest speaker and best practices industry advisor for equity, diversity and inclusion, Ms. McIntosh is passionate about creating a respectful workplace and best practices for all applicants and employees.

Ms. McIntosh is also passionate about personal and professional development. As a community educator, she inspires women of all ages and at-risk youth to use obstacles as stepping stones toward their GREATNESS. She is a certified Professional Woman Network trainer for women's issues, with an emphasis on Self-Esteem and Empowerment for Women, and Leadership Skills for Women.

Ms. McIntosh is featured as a co-author in 3 previously released books with PWN; *Self-Esteem & Empowerment for Women; The Young Women's Guide for Personal Success; and Learning to Love Yourself; Self-Esteem for Women.*

Ms. McIntosh is a graduate of Bethel University where attained the following degrees: Associates of Arts; Bachelor of Arts in Organizational Leadership; and a Master of Arts in Strategic Leadership.

Contact:
Yolanda Y. McIntosh
651.200.2131
heysistagirl732@gmail.com

TWENTY-SEVEN

What's Your Secret?

Yolanda McIntosh

Hey! Sister Girl, you got a few minutes? Here, have a seat. Get comfortable. Let's sip some tea and chat for a while. I noticed a few things about you and I am wondering, *what's your secret?* Yes, what's **your** secret? How do you do it? How do you make it all happen with such finesse? I mean, when I see you, I see a woman so well put together. You have it all and you balance it so well. You're a companion, a mother, a sister, a friend, a business owner, a prayer intercessor, an employee, and an advocate. You appear to maneuver through the various roles and responsibilities so seamlessly. You do it all and I am curious to know:

What's your secret? **How do you make it all happen?**

_____

_____

Such external roles are noble and wholesome; full of strength and resilience. And if you are like me, it is what I want others to see when they encounter me. But, since it's just you and I, chatting; as sister girls, can I be transparent with you? I have a secret and I am wondering if you will be my confidant?

In spite of my many successes, accomplishments and accolades, things for me aren't always how they appear. You know what? Maybe now is not the right time for me to share. I do not want to take up much of your time. Look, I have trust issues so I really need to know that I can share my secret in a safe space. I need to know that I can trust you. Is that ok? I'm going to trust that it is. Thank you for creating a safe space. Let's continue.

As I was saying, what is seen on the outside is not always a reflection of what is happening on the inside. On the outside, I appear confident, focused, driven, passionate and compassionate. While, those external behaviors are genuine most of the time; there are times, on the inside, when I secretly struggle mentally and emotionally with areas that are present, but not as visible; areas that I hide deep beneath the surface of the iceberg from others and oftentimes I hide from myself. Some of the mental and emotional areas I hide include:

My body image and the transition it is going through; insecurity about my self- worth stemming from a dysfunctional childhood; fear of rejection resulting in an inability to set healthy and appropriate boundaries in relationships; the fear of being judged by others if they were aware or could see my vulnerabilities; fear of facing the reality that, oftentimes, I am not as strong as I portray myself to be; fear of accepting myself for who I am just as I am; fear of liking and loving myself with no strings attached; and the fear of not being good enough for myself and others.

Sister Girl, can you relate? Are there times when what you portray on the outside is not a reflection of what is really going on inside? If so, what does that look like for you?

_____

_____

Thank you for sharing and allowing yourself to be vulnerable with me. I do not take your trust for granted. As we continue our chat, would you like some more tea? Coming right up!

Sometimes it seems as though we, as a society of women, are pitted against one another without taking the time to get to know each other. It's like we are programmed to cast judgement towards each other because of our differences. I wonder what would happen if we adjusted the lens of our perceptions to instead see our differences as uniqueness. Would it change the view of how we see one another as women? Hmmm. Let's sip on this thought for a bit before responding.

What do you think would happen if we, as a society of women, exchanged our lens of differences for the lens of uniqueness?

_____

_____

What step/s do you think would be necessary to start the lens transition?

_____

_____

What would it take to sustain momentum?

_____

_____

Sister Girl, this is good stuff! Yes, both the tea and processing through this chatting session.

Oh, it's my turn? Alright, here it is.

New Labels/New Lens

Oftentimes, we define ourselves by the labels assigned to us through the lens of others; through their view of us based on how <u>they</u> see the world. Some of the lenses others see us through include: the lens of <u>their</u> family structure; the lens of <u>their</u> culture; the lens of <u>their</u> religious or lack of religious culture; the lens of societal norms where <u>they</u> reside; and the lens of <u>their</u> personal experiences that often are not in direct relation to an experience with us. But, it is their lens and <u>if we are not careful, we will mimic labels assigned to us; but not by us.</u> Do you see the pattern? Now I wonder…if we assign labels to ourselves, what angle of the lens would we view ourselves from? Better yet. <u>Best case scenario</u>:

If you were to assign empowering labels to yourself, what words would you use to describe you?

_____

_____

What angle/s of the lens would <u>you</u> view yourself from?

_____

_____

What would need to happen for you to live through the positive angle/s of your own lens?

_____

_____

What positive steps could you take today?

_____

_____

How will you track your progress?

_____

_____

Do you have a sister girl/s you can trust with your secret/s and who would be able to support you during this label/lens transition? If so, name her/ them below:

_____

_____

External Conqueror/Internal Warrior

Whew, Sister Girl! We are really getting it in, aren't we? The truth is - the external conqueror we portray on the outside, is the result of the internal warrior within. It is the internal warrior that is buried deep down in our core, beneath the labels others have placed on us, trying to press her way through. Trying to press through the muck and mire of the challenges, setbacks and battles we face in life. What people may label as "being fake", is actually the internal warrior fighting to get to the surface. The internal warrior will not give up! And neither should you! The internal warrior wants to merge her inner core with her external self. She is fighting for alignment. She knows once she removes from her focus the labels and the lenses of others, she will soar! She also knows fighting the battle won't be easy. But she is determined to fight in order to win the war! And now that I think about it; she reminds me of you!

What are you determined to fight through internally so your inner core can be in alignment with your external conqueror? Feel free to have another sip of tea before responding. This is another thought that might take a minute.

_____

_____

What additional steps can you think of to free your inner warrior so you can win the war and show up in full authenticity?

_____

_____

What would it take to sustain momentum?

_____

_____

As we wrap up our sister time together, is there more you would like to share that I may not have asked?

_____

_____

Secret Takeaways

Sister Girl! Thank you for our chat and tea. It was so refreshing to be transparent and vulnerable in sharing my secrets without judgement and created by the safe space I needed. And, I was strengthened by your courage to do the same. I understand it may not have been easy for you to share, but you trusted me with your secrets anyway. That really means a lot.

Sister Girl. I want you to know, through our sharing, it was encouraging to learn that I am not the only one who appears so strong and so well put together on the outside, but struggles with insecurities and areas of brokenness that are not always so easy to detect or heal.

What stood out to me the most, Sister Girl, was the reminder of the inner warrior we both carry! How our inner self continues to press through the pain of our internal war and our struggle to not be defined by the labels and lenses of others. We now know that it is up to us to define ourselves through our own lens; and we have the power to do so. We now realize, what others may label as us "being fake" is often our internal warrior attempting to align with our external conqueror. I also gained respect for the fact, based on your responses, that although our methods of expression might be different, our desire for victory is the same. For me, our chat is the start of my healing process; my walk into full authenticity.

What was our chat like for you?

_____

_____

Sister Girl. As you take this journey towards realigning your internal warrior with your external conqueror by connecting with your inner self at its core, know that you are not on this journey alone. I am walking right alongside you, believing in you, praying for you and congratulating you on your victory – in advance! Here's to walking in the full armor of authenticity!

Signed, Your Secret Sister Girl!

Yolanda Y. McIntosh

Notes:

_____

_____

_____

_____

_____

_____

_____

_____

_____

_____

_____

_____

_____

_____

_____

_____

_____

_____

_____

_____

_____

_____

THE PROFESSIONAL WOMAN NETWORK
Training and Certification of Women's Issues

 Linda Ellis Eastman, President & CEO of The Professional Woman Network, has trained and certified over two thousand individuals to start their own consulting/seminar business. Women from such countries as Brazil, Argentia, the Bahamas, Costa Rica, Bermuda, Nigeria, South Africa, Malaysia, and Mexico have attended trainings.

Topics of certification include:
• Diversity & Multiculturalism
• Woman's Issues
• Women: A Journey to Wellness
• Save Our Youth
• Teen Image & Social Etiquette
• Leadership & Empowerment Skills for Youth
• Customer Service & Professionalism
• Marketing a Consulting Practice
• Professional Coaching
• Professional Presentation Skills

If you are interested in learning more about becoming certified or about starting your own consulting/seminar business contact:

The Professional Woman Network
P.O. Box 333
Prospect, KY 40059
(502) 345-4139
lindaeastman@prodigy.net
www.prowoman.net

Women's Empowerment Series

The Total Woman

Women of Courage: Volume III

Women of Courage: Volume II

Women of Courage

Leading from the Heart

Breaking the Concrete Ceiling: Emmpowerment Tools for Women

Finding Your Voice: The Assertive & Empowered Woman

The Female Factor

The Coaching Guru II

Your Personal GPS: How to Navigate Life's Challenges & Roadblocks

The Female Architect: How to Rebuild Your Life

The Self-Esteem Guide for Women

Women Power: Strategies for Female Leaders

Teenage Girls: Self-Esteem, Communication & Confidence

The Female CEO Pearls, Power & Passion

Overcoming the Good Little Girl Syndrome

The Empowered Woman: Purpose, Passion & Possibilities

The POWER of Transformation: Reinventing Your Life

Baby Boomers: Secrets for Life After 50!

The Female Leader: Empowerment, Confidence & Passion

What's the Difference? Embracing Diversity & Inclusivity

The Young Professional Woman: Breaking Into the Business World & Succeeding

A View from the Top: Exceptional Leadership Strategies

Getting Well: Mind, Body & Spirit

How to Break the Glass Ceiling Without a Hammer

Breaking Free: Overcoming Self-Sabotage

Creating a Blueprint for Inner Change: Tools for Personal Growth
How to Survive When Your Ship is Sinking: Weathering Life's Storms
Leader in Pearls: How to Be a Change Architect
Celebration of Life: Inspiration for Women
Releasing Strongholds: Letting Go of What's Holding You Back
The Power of a Woman: Embracing the Woman Within
The Power of Change: Reinvent Yourself at Any Age
Life is an Attitude. The Power of Positive Thinking
Transformation: Reinventing the Woman Within
The Self-Architect: Redesigning Your Life
Becoming Your Own Best Friend
The Woman's Handbook for Self-Empowerment
Remove the Mask! Living an Authentic Life
The Woman's Handbook for Self-Confidence
A Journey Within: Self-Discovery for Women
Learning to Love Yourself: Self-Esteem for Women

The African American Library
The Black Female Leader
The Professional Black Woman
Sister to Sister A Guide for African American Girls
Bruised But Not Broken
Learning to Love Yourself: A Handbook for the African American Woman
Wellness for the African American Woman: Mind, Body & Spirit
Life Skills for the African American Woman
Raising African American Boys

Raising African American Girls
Living Your Vision and Purpose

The Professional Woman Network - Book Series
Becoming the Professional Woman
Customer Service & Professionalism for Women
Self-Esteem & Empowerment for Women
The Young Woman's Guide for Personal Success
The Christian Woman's Guide for Personal Success
Survival Skills for the African-American Woman
Overcoming the SuperWoman Syndrome
You're on Stage! Image, Etiquette, Branding & Style
Women's Journey to Wellness: Mind, Body & Spirit
A Woman's Survival Guide for Obstacles, Transition & Change
Women as Leaders: Strategies for Empowerment & Communication
Beyond the Body! Developing Inner Beauty
The Young Man's Guide for Personal Success
Emotional Wellness for Women Volume I
Emotional Wellness for Women Volume II
Emotional Wellness for Women Volume III
The Baby Boomer's Handbook for Women

Christian Series
The Power of God
The Power of God: Daily Devotional
The Power of God: Daily Devotional II

These books are available from the individual contributors, the publisher (www.pwnbooks.com), www.amazon.com, and your local bookstore by request.